COPPER LODGE LIBRARY

NEW WORLD ECHOES

COMPILATION AND INTRODUCTION BY
Jennifer Courtney

MULTIMEDIA

New World Echoes (Copper Lodge Library)
© 2020 Classical Conversations® MultiMedia. All rights reserved.

Published by Classical Conversations, Inc.
255 Air Tool Drive
Southern Pines, NC 28387

CLASSICALCONVERSATIONS.COM
CLASSICALCONVERSATIONSBOOKS.COM

Cover design by Classical Conversations.

The cover artwork and illustrations were collected from a variety of illustrators.

Please note that the original, unconventional spelling and punctuation are retained in this compilation of stories and poems. In order to keep the tall tales family friendly, some portions have been intentionally omitted.

Printed in the United States of America

ISBN: 978-1-7329640-4-4

ACKNOWLEDGMENTS

Since childhood, I have loved stories—stories from around the world that my family read to me, and stories from our own family that they told to me. I'm grateful to my parents and grandparents for these precious memories.

I knew this book would be the most challenging in this series, but I also knew it would be the most rewarding in the end. It was a joy to honor the literary contributions of the "young" countries that make up the New World.

Thanks to…

Leigh Bortins for being excited about this project with me while we were swimming in the lake.

Heather Shirley for loving beautiful stories and supporting this book.

Jen Greenholt for digging up the hard sources and supporting me all the way.

Kathi James for making the book beautiful and loving stories as much as I do.

Leslie Hubbard for finding numerous stories and poems for me. Your perseverance will bless many.

Cyndi Widman for thoughtfully editing so that my words are clear and meaningful.

Jeremiah Wentz for keeping us on track so that the dream of this book could become a reality.

My children (Ben, Abby, Susannah, and Mia), who have been my read-aloud companions for many years, and, especially, my husband, Tim, for listening patiently as I struggled to find just the right stories.

Lastly, thanks to families everywhere who take time each day to curl up with their children and share a great story. You are building a beautiful life.

TABLE OF CONTENTS

Superheroes and Security Blankets 9

How to Savor This Book..13

WEEK ONE

Mudjee Monedo *(Retold by K. Pyle)* 19

The King of the Buffaloes *(Retold by K. Pyle)* 27

POEM: The Buffalo Trail *(C. B. Clark)*....................................33

WEEK TWO

How the Bear Family Got Its Name *(Retold by M. F. Washburne)*....35

The Boy Who Set a Snare for the Sun *(Retold by C. Mathews)*..........41

POEM: The Pleiades *(A. Lowell)* 45

WEEK THREE

The Frogs and the Crane *(Retold by C. and E. Eastman)*....................47

Great Heart and the Three Tests *(Retold by C. Macmillan)*...............51

POEM: The Sandpiper *(C. Thaxter)* 57

WEEK FOUR

How Rabbit Deceived Fox *(Retold by C. Macmillan)* 59

How Raven Brought Fire to the Indians *(Retold by C. Macmillan)* ..67

POEM: In the Garden *(E. Dickinson)*..75

WEEK FIVE

White Plume *(Retold by M. L. McLaughlin)*...........................77

The Child of the Evening Star *(Retold by W. T. Larned)* 87

POEM: The Arrow and the Song *(H. W. Longfellow)* 97

WEEK SIX

The Little Boy and Girl in the Clouds *(Retold by W. T. Larned)*........99

The Fairy Bride *(Retold by W. T. Larned)*............................. 105

POEM: The Cloud *(S. Teasdale)*... 113

WEEK SEVEN

The Peterkins Try to Become Wise *(L. P. Hale)*................................. 115

Old Johnny Appleseed *(E. Harrison)*.................................... 119

POEM: September *(H. H. Jackson)*.. 123

WEEK EIGHT

The Young Robin Who Was Afraid to Fly *(C. D. Pierson)* 125

Little Benjamin *(L. E. Richards)*.. 131

POEM: Eletelephony *(L. E. Richards)*... 143

WEEK NINE

Nelly's Hospital *(L. M. Alcott)*... 145

How the Animals Lost Their Tails and Got Them Back Traveling
    From Philadelphia to Medicine Hat *(C. Sandburg)* 161

POEM: Fog *(C. Sandburg)*.. 169

WEEK TEN

The First Thanksgiving *(A. F. Blaisdell and F. K. Ball)*...................... 171

POEM: The Pumpkin *(J. G. Whittier)*.. 175

WEEK ELEVEN

The Baby-House *(P. Parley)*... 177

A Case of Coincidence *(R. T. Cooke)*.. 183

POEM: Colorado Snow-Birds *(H. H. Jackson)* 193

WEEK TWELVE

Christmas at Red Butte *(L. M. Montgomery)*...................................... 197

POEM: A Visit from St. Nicholas *(by C. C. Moore)* 205

WEEK THIRTEEN

Crockett's Fight With a Catfish *(D. Crockett)*..................................... 209

The Heroine of Kaintuck *(D. Crockett)* 211

POEM: The Frost *(H. F. Gould))* 215

WEEK FOURTEEN

Mrs. Cuttle and the Catamount *(D. Crockett)*.................................... 217

Katy Goodgrit and the Wolves *(D. Crockett)* 221

POEM: Home, Sweet Home *(J. H. Payne)*... 223

WEEK FIFTEEN

The Saga of Pecos Bill *(E. O'Reilly,* ABRIDGED*)* 227

The Life and Adventures of Calamity Jane *(Calamity Jane)*............ 233

POEM: John Henry *(Retold by J. H. Combs)*....................................... 239

WEEK SIXTEEN

    Paul Bunyan's Family and Inventions *(W. B. Laughead, ABR.)* 241

    Paul Bunyan's Animals and Insects *(W. B. Laughead, ABR.)* 251

    POEM: Barbara Frietchie *(J. G. Whittier)* 259

WEEK SEVENTEEN

    Feeding Paul Bunyan's Crew *(W. B. Laughead, ABRIDGED)* 263

    The Glorious Whitewasher *(M. Twain)* 267

    POEM: Casey Jones *(W. Saunders)* 273

WEEK EIGHTEEN

    Joe Mufferaw *(Translated and adapted by J. Courtney)* 275

    Crooked Mick *(Compiled and embellished by J. Courtney)* 283

    POEM: O Captain! My Captain! *(W. Whitman)* 287

WEEK NINETEEN

    Why the Tiger and the Stag Fear Each Other

        (Retold by E. S. Eells) 289

    How the Toad Got His Bruises *(Retold by E. S. Eells)* 293

    POEM: An Evening at the Farm *(J. T. Trowbridge)* 297

WEEK TWENTY

    Francisco's Home *(E. C. Brooks)* 299

    The Plumed Serpent, Quetzalcoatl *(F. E. Wait)* 305

    POEM: My Nicaragua *(S. de la Selva)* 311

WEEK TWENTY-ONE

    The Naming of the Birds *(Retold by K. B. Judson)* 313

    The Fisherman Who Caught the Sun *(Retold by O. B. Miller)* 315

    POEM: Sea Shell *(A. Lowell)* 319

WEEK TWENTY-TWO

    Charlotte's Quest *(L. M. Montgomery)* 321

    The Money-Chest *(J. Arnason)* 337

    POEM: The Night Cometh *(A. L. Walker)* 341

WEEK TWENTY-THREE

    Tereté, the Boy in the Moon *(Retold by K. M. Clark)* 343

    The Grave *(S. Jones)* 347

    POEM: The Kind Moon *(S. Teasdale)* 349

WEEK TWENTY-FOUR

    King Dunce *(A. Westbury)* 351

    Goolayyahlee the Pelican *(Retold by K. L. Parker)* 357

    POEM: The Maranoa Drovers *(A. B. Paterson)* 361

Works Cited 363

SUPERHEROES AND SECURITY BLANKETS

When my children were small, they lived out this curious mix every day. Some of them lived in capes, dashing around the house to save the world. At certain times of day, though, they craved the comfort of their security blankets and a quiet time in the rocking chair with me. They are eager to charge out into the wide world and make their way, and they are eager for the comforts of home.

As I gathered the stories for this little book, it occurred to me that these two things—superheroes and security blankets—offer a good summary of the types of stories that were born out of the New World. As men and women spread out into strange and dangerous new territories, they often had to don their superhero capes and muster their strengths and resources. Out of these adventures came stories of men and women like Paul Bunyan, Pecos Bill, Katy Goodgrit, Joe Mufferaw, Calamity Jane, and Crooked Mick. Because the pioneers faced dangerous and threatening surroundings, tales of superheroes offered a measure of comfort and humor. The stories gave hope that people could survive and even thrive in these wild territories. These characters paved the way for the flood of superhero movies on the market today. Sometimes, the threats came from industrialization and mechanization, leading to tragic figures like John Henry and Casey Jones. These ballads sang the death of the old way of agrarian life and paved the way for a new world of working alongside machines. The same kind of stories are echoed today in any of number of "man versus the machine" books and movies.

With all of these dangers and bewildering changes, folks in the nineteenth century in the New World loved stories about the comforts of home. These stories, which often involve love-starved orphans being welcomed into a home and family, provide moments of peace and gentility. For the first time in history, writers in the nineteenth century wrote for children as their primary audience. The popularity of children's books and magazines exploded. Authors often wrote moral tales to guide children toward virtuous choices. They extolled both the values and safety of home, family, church, and community.

In addition to the superheroes and security blankets, there are also myths and legends told by the native peoples who had inhabited North and South America and Australia. These stories have much in common with ancient Greek and Roman mythology, which attempted to explain the origins of things or to present the figure of the ideal warrior. Echoes of creation and heroes resound across space and time.

As different as they are, these stories echo one another, and they even echo the stories found in *Old World Echoes*. We named the books in this series *Echoes* to illustrate the joy of hearing the echoes that reverberate throughout the story of mankind. Children love to shout and hear their own echoes. Children thrill to physical echoes; they can also thrill to literary echoes. Just as it is exciting to hear the echoes, it is sad to miss them if you do not know the original stories. As we read aloud the stories that have formed our culture, we hear more and more echoes; literature becomes richer and richer the more we are able to hear.

In this volume, I have included stories from Native American tribes of both the United States and Canada. I have selected traditional children's stories from the nineteenth century from the United States and Canada. I have hunted down tall tales that tell of the men and women who carved out a life in wild, new places. I have digitally traveled around the New World to gather stories from Iceland, New Zealand, the Caribbean, Brazil, Nicaragua, Mexico, Alaska, Hawaii, and Australia. The range is great, from ancient Native American, Brazilian, and Maori stories that sought to preserve an ideal of bravery to the children's magazine stories that sought to help children be good by modeling sacrificial choices. I endeavored to find stories that would appeal to both young and old, male and female, timid and bold.

Although some of these stories have a uniquely New World tang, many of these stories resemble oral tales that were told in the Ancient World and in the Old World. The echo of human experience sounds on and on.

These stories are not just bedtime stories for children. Indeed, the whole family can relish the tales of heroism and self-sacrifice, of loyalty and lifelong friendships, of providential rescues by supernatural helpers, of cunning adaptations to new environments, of the comfort of home, family, and holidays, and of growing into one's adult responsibilities. *New World Echoes* can be read with the whole family as a discussion starter.

One other note about reading aloud as a family: literature reflects the nature of a fallen world. As such, stories often tell of dark or difficult situations. Even when we are reading Old Testament stories from children's Bibles, it does not take long before we encounter the darkness of Adam and Eve succumbing to Satan, of Cain killing Abel, or of Joseph's brothers casting him into the well. The same is true of some of the stories in this volume. These stories give concrete form to emotions and abstractions, to our hopes and fears.

Although we want to protect our children, we cannot sanitize the world for them. We cannot sanitize the stories we use to teach them about the world. As G. K. Chesterton writes:

> Fairy tales, then, are not responsible for producing in children fear, or any of the shapes of fear; fairy tales do not give the child the idea of the evil or the ugly; that is in the child already, because it is in the world already. Fairy tales do not give the child his first idea of bogey. What fairy tales give the child is his first clear idea of the possible defeat of bogey. The baby has known the dragon intimately ever since he had an imagination. What the fairy tale provides for him is a St. George to kill the dragon.

> Exactly what the fairy tale does is this: it accustoms him for a series of clear pictures to the idea that these limitless terrors

had a limit, that these shapeless enemies have enemies in the knights of God, that there is something in the universe more mystical than darkness, and stronger than strong fear." (*Tremendous Trifles*, 1909)

The truth is that we do have an enemy and that we do have a Savior. We should train ourselves to step forth bravely, willing to sacrifice ourselves for others, and always on the lookout to be rescued by our Savior and Friend.

The echoes of fairy tales are perhaps more needed in our day than ever before. Our children are being raised in a culture that tells them that every individual should decide what is best for themselves. Fairy tales argue that virtue lies in the common good and often makes us subdue our whims and passions in order to love our neighbors well. Because there was a break in the tradition, sometimes our culture echoes the past without knowing what it means. Let us reject this world in which everything is an echo with no substance. Rather, let us embrace the old tradition of fairy tales that argued that the world is a mysterious place. The ability to accept the mystery nurtures faith, hope, and love. Like little children, we must believe that miracles happen and that the unseen is palpably real. As my friend Jen argues, "Postmodernism says we only ever see in a glass darkly. Scripture tells us that we only see in a glass darkly temporarily."

Remember, too, that the echo is not an end, it is a beginning. We can keep it running through the ages, but it will fade unless we take up the chant again. It is my prayer that this book will start the echo for a new generation; for, although the times and people change, the echoes of truth, goodness, and beauty will continue to reverberate through the ages.

—Jennifer Courtney

HOW TO SAVOR THIS BOOK

This book is designed to give you one or two classic stories and a poem to read aloud and relish with your whole family each week (yes, even with the high schoolers and adults). This book is NOT designed to burden an already full homeschool day but to provide a beautiful space to gather as a family for about thirty minutes to read and discuss together. My family likes to gather first thing in the morning with a delicious breakfast and beautiful stories. In the warm weather, we read outside. In the winter, we cozy up around the fire. Other families may like to read around the dinner table or in mom and dad's bed. If you only get to one story this week, that is terrific.

Do not be easily discouraged. Even if you only have time to read the stories and poems, you are relishing beauty together. For the glorious days when you have time to dig deeper, the following guide will help you discuss the stories with your family and recite and delight in the poetry. Let's walk through the 5 Core Habits of Grammar and the 5 Common Topics with a story from the book.

5 CORE HABITS OF GRAMMAR

The 5 Core Habits are skills that can help us all to engage with, and thus to enjoy, a good story. The following example from "How the Bear Family Got Its Name" lists ways to practice these habits as you read and discuss stories with your family.

NAMING

Young children like to learn the names of things: the characters, magical creatures, and enchanted weapons. After listening closely, they can tell you the names of people and places they remember. Older children can attend to the meaning attached to these names.

Example: Who was in this story? The Indian tribe, the orphan boy, the mother bear, and her two cubs. What do the names in your family mean? If you were to choose an animal name for your family, what would it be? Why?

ATTENDING

Young children will often attend better to the surface details of the stories than older children and adults. This is excellent because those surface details will contribute to the deep meaning of each story. Help them attend to patterns like repeated phrases or the number of days. Encourage them to engage all five main senses.

Setting: When and where does this story take place?

Draw out the details using their five senses. What do dried meat and berries taste like? What color were the woods at this season? What did it smell like in the forest? What do you think it sounded like when the three children (cubs) were playing together? What do you think it looked like when the mother bear threw fish to her cubs?

Characters: Who are the people in this story? (see Naming)

Plot: Can you tell me the main things that happen in the story? Does this remind you of other stories or movies?

Conflict: What is the main struggle the character faces or problem he or she must solve?

How does the character solve the problem?

Example: The orphan boy is lost. He is adopted and raised by a mother bear. The Indian hunters take him back to their village. He must learn to behave as a human again.

Theme: Did the characters in the story learn a lesson? Did you?

MEMORIZING

Young children first build their language skills through memorizing. This is how they learned to speak their mother tongue. They will likely memorize and retell many of these stories. Their memorization of poetry will be aided by rhythm, rhyme, and repetition. Be sure to read the poem aloud several times each week. Have them make up a tune or pat out a rhythm on their lap to help them remember.

EXPRESSING

Young children have very active bodies that are intimately connected to their minds. Here are several ways for them to express what they have learned from your reading:

Recitation: Have a formal recitation at the end of the year in which they deliver memorized poems to the grandparents, or use the poems as presentations in your Classical Conversations Foundations community.

Narration: Give the children a few minutes to tell back the story or poem they have just heard. This is an exercise called *narration*. Putting the story into their own words makes it theirs. Other children can add missed details, or you can ask questions to help them fill in some gaps.

Acting: Allow the children to act out the story throughout the week. They will almost always find simple costumes and props around the house to add to the fun.

Drawing: Children often attend better to read-alouds if their hands are busy. They can illustrate the stories and poems while you read.

Copywork: Have the children copy the poetry in their best handwriting and then illustrate them. It will be a keepsake to treasure.

STORYTELLING

Children love to tell stories. They can re-tell the stories and poems you are reading to them. Allow them to be creative, changing the setting or plot or characters. Many will likely be inspired to write their own fairy tales, myths, legends, and poems.

5 COMMON TOPICS

There is a relatively simple set of questions that you can practice as a family to help them contemplate meaning. (For more on the 5 Common Topics, read *The Question: Teaching Your Child the Essentials of Classical Education* by Leigh Bortins.)

DEFINITION

What is a thing and what are its parts? Who is a character? What groups of people does he belong to? What distinguishes him from other members in the group?

For example, you can take one of the characters and list every trait they have in order to get a unique and precise definition. You could define the orphan boy as an early Native American who gets lost in the woods and is adopted by a bear family before he returns to his village and must learn to behave as a human again.

Have fun with this exercise by including as many characteristics as your children can find.

COMPARISON

How are two characters or situations the same? How are they different?

Compare this story to another story of a human being adopted by animals such as *Tarzan* or *The Jungle Book*.

What characteristics do the humans and animals have that are the same? Different? (Who are they?) How do they behave the same? Differently? (What do they do?)

CIRCUMSTANCES

What else is going on in the world?

Closely examining the circumstances in which a character has been placed helps us to understand the decisions they make and to empathize with them. For example, think about the circumstances for the boy. He needs a family to care for him, and the bears are willing and able. He needs food and shelter, and he learns to obtain these things as a bear would.

Unpacking the circumstances helps us to empathize with others and to attempt to make the wisest decisions we can. Encourage your children to think about how both the bears and the Native Americans felt in this story.

RELATIONSHIP

What happened before? After? What are the causes and effects?

What happened before the boy was adopted by the bear cubs? He was lost, alone, hungry, and unprotected. What happened after? He was cared for and loved, having not just food and shelter, but a home and a family to belong to. What happened after that? He returned to his village, and the bears returned to their life in the woods. And then? He refused to hunt bears for the remainder of his life. What do you think will happen after the story? Do you think there will be more or less peace between the bears and the Native Americans?

Peering into the causes and effects of other characters' decisions allows us to practice for the big choices we will face. We can learn to weigh the consequences (effects) through story long before we face weighty choices in our own lives.

TESTIMONY

Who has something to say about this? Are they trustworthy?

The boy must trade the authority of his bear mother for the authority of his human tribe. How does he know that this is fitting? How does he know to trust his people?

From the evening news to the internet, our children will be bombarded with people who claim to be authorities in their lives. Through story, we can teach them to evaluate whether these authorities and witnesses are reliable and trustworthy so that they can decide whether to accept or reject them.

Sometimes your family will want to ask lots of questions about a story. Other times, you may only have time to just pick up the book and read. That is valuable, too. Delight in the sounds of the words and lose yourselves in the story. Like children who delight in the echoes they create, I hope you will fill your home with echoes this year.

Week One:

MUDJEE MONEDO

Native North American Legend

RETOLD BY KATHARINE PYLE

Upon the banks of the broad Ogechee River there once stood a little Indian village. The people who lived there were prosperous and happy. There were fish in the river and game in the forest, and no one lacked for anything.

But after a time a terrible misfortune fell upon the people. An ogre named Mudjee Monedo came to live near them. Upon an open plain he laid out a racecourse, and it was his amusement to challenge the young men of the village to race with him there. None dared to refuse, for the ogre was cruel and revengeful, and they feared what he might do to the old men and children if they should refuse; and yet to race with him meant death.

"Life against life," the ogre would cry, laying his hand on the goal-post. "My life in wager against yours. This post is the goal, yonder charred stump the turning-point. The loser pays the forfeit with his life."

But none of the Indian warriors ever could win in that race with Mudjee Monedo. The ogre had the power to turn himself at will into any four-footed animal that he might choose. If he found he was being outstripped in the race he would change himself into a wolf, a deer, or a buffalo, and so easily win the race against the swiftest runner of them all. So, one after another, the finest young men of the village were slain at the goal-post.

A deep gloom settled over those who were still left alive. They would have taken their wives and children and gone elsewhere to live, but they knew the ogre would follow on their tracks. Their only hope was that some time a warrior might rise among them who would be able to outwit the ogre and win the race.

Somewhat away from the other lodges, and in the shadow of the forest, lived a widow with a daughter and a young son. This son was a boy of twelve named Manedowa. The widow's husband and her ten eldest sons had all raced with the ogre at one time or another, and all had paid the forfeit with their lives. Now Manedowa was fast growing tall and manly. Instead of being glad of this the widow was terrified. She dreaded the time when the ogre might think the boy old enough to race with him. Already Mudjee Monedo had his eye upon him. Often he would make some excuse to come to the lodge when the boy was busy there. Then the ogre would look him up and down.

"You are growing fast," he would say. "You will make a famous runner. Some time you must come and look at my racecourse. Perhaps we may even run a friendly race together—though I am growing too old and stiff to have any chance against young limbs like yours."

Then the widow would shudder and make some excuse to send the boy away out of sight. She knew that when he was fully grown it would not be for long that the ogre would spare him.

One day the boy was away fishing and the widow and her daughter were busy in the lodge together. Suddenly a shadow fell across the floor. They looked up in terror, expecting to see the ogre peering in. Instead, a handsome young warrior stood there in the doorway. He was a stranger. They had never seen him before. The sunshine played upon his shining limbs like fire. His eyes were bright and piercing, and above his forehead waved a plume of gorgeous feathers. For a moment he stood looking in upon them. Then he laid a deer down upon the threshold, and silently turned and disappeared in the green depths of the forest.

Wondering, the mother and her daughter stared after him. They did not know who he could be. They waited for some time, and then, as he did not return, they cut up the deer and hung it up to dry.

Two days after this the stranger again came to the lodge. As silently as before he laid a bear down before them, and again disappeared among the thickets; but that night they heard the sound of his pipe not far from the lodge; it was a love song to the girl that he was playing.

The next evening he came again, bringing more game, but this time he entered and sat down. After that he stayed in the widow's lodge, and the girl became his wife. She was very happy, for no other hunter brought home such fine game as he, and no other was as handsome and as noble-looking.

Every morning he went away, gliding off silently into the depths of the forest and disappearing from their sight. Where he went they did not know, but every night he came again, bringing to them the choicest of game and fish. The plume above his forehead shone with strange colours, and sometimes it seemed as though the light about him came from himself, and not from the sunshine or the firelight. Neither the girl nor her mother dared to question him as to who he was or whence he came.

With so much game hanging about the lodge it was not long before Mudjee Monedo grew suspicious. He suspected that some warrior had come to live with the widow and her daughter and that they were hiding it from him. Often he stole up silently to the lodge hoping to find the hunter there, but he never saw him. At last he questioned the widow openly.

"All this game," he said, trying to smile at her pleasantly, "where does it come from?"

The widow began to tremble. "My son—" she began.

"Your son!" interrupted the Magician. "Do you mean to tell me that your son could shoot a bear or a buffalo such as I have seen here?"

"He is very large and strong for his age," said the poor widow.

"If he is old enough to shoot such game he is old enough to race with me," cried the ogre. "I will come again when he is at home, and he and I will talk of it."

The Mudjee Monedo turned on his heel and strode away through the forest, breaking the young trees and muttering to himself as he went.

The widow and her daughter were almost dead with fright. If they told the ogre of the strange warrior who had come to live in their lodge he would without doubt challenge the stranger to race with him. If they did not, it would be the boy who would be slain.

That night when the hunter returned as usual with his game the widow told him of all that had happened—of how Mudjee Monedo had come to the lodge and questioned her, of how she had pretended it was her son who had shot the game, and of the threat that the ogre had used.

The warrior listened to all she had to say in silence. When she had ended he answered calmly, "It is well. I will run a race with this Mudjee Monedo. To-morrow he will come this way again. Then ask him to stop and eat with you, and I too will be here."

His wife and her mother began to beg and implore him not to let the Magician see him, but he silenced them. "Let it be as I say," said he. "To-morrow do you put corn meal and herbs in a pot to cook, and add to it three birch buds. Mudjee Monedo and I will eat of it together."

The next morning very early the ogre appeared at the lodge door, but the stranger had already gone into the forest. Mudjee Monedo looked about him and saw all the fresh meat. "Truly your son has become a mighty hunter," he sneered.

"No, Mudjee Monedo," answered the widow. "I knew it was useless to try to deceive you. It is not my son, but my son-in-law, who has shot all this game. He is a mighty warrior. He will soon return from the forest. Sit down, and when he comes you can eat together."

"Did I not know it?" cried the ogre triumphantly. "No one may hope to deceive Mudjee Monedo for long."

He entered the lodge and sat down. He had not been there long before the stranger appeared in the doorway. The brave was in the full dress of a warrior. Across his forehead was a broad band of red paint, and the feathers above his forehead were red and blue. The ogre's eyes glistened at the sight of him. The hunter greeted Mudjee Monedo, and sat down not far from him.

Presently, while his wife and mother-in-law made ready the food, he and the ogre talked. Soon Mudjee Monedo asked the warrior whether he would not run a race with him upon his racecourse.

Calmly the stranger agreed.

"But I am growing old," said Mudjee Monedo slyly. "I am not strong and tireless as I was once. Because of that, if I race with you you must let me set the wager."

To this, also, the stranger agreed. Then the food was ready, and he courteously asked Mudjee Monedo to eat with him. The ogre could not refuse, but when he saw the dish that was set before them he became very uneasy. Well he knew that for him there was evil in that food. The strange warrior, however, took no notice of his confusion. He dipped into the dish and ate of it, and Mudjee Monedo was obliged to do likewise, though the herbs that were in it tickled his throat and set him coughing.

Finally the warrior lifted the dish, drank deep of it, and handed it to the other. The ogre hesitated a moment. The broth was hateful to him, but he was afraid to refuse. In haste to be done with it he raised it to his mouth and swallowed what was left of it at one gulp.

Suddenly he coughed and choked. One of the birch buds at the bottom of the pot had lodged in his windpipe. His face turned purple and his eyes seemed starting from their sockets. He got to his feet and staggered out into the open air. A moment he turned and tried to speak, but a violent fit of coughing stopped him, and he hurried away through the thickets, still wheezing and choking as he went.

By the next day the news had gone through the village that a strange warrior was to run a race with Mudjee Monedo, and a great crowd gathered on the hills near by to see the race.

When the stranger appeared upon the course a murmur of wonder arose. Never had the people seen such a warrior before. He was taller by a head than the tallest youth in the village, and his feet scarce seemed to touch the earth, so lightly did he walk. Then hope sprang up in the people's hearts. Might it not be that this wondrous stranger would in some way win the race and free them from the power of the ogre.

Mudjee Monedo looked about him at the waiting people, and seemed to read what was in their hearts. His lips drew back in a cruel smile. Then he laid his hand upon the goal-post.

"You have let me choose my own wager," he cried aloud, so that all might hear what he said to the stranger. "It is this: life against life; my life against yours. This post is the goal, yonder charred stump the turning-point. The loser pays the forfeit."

"So be it," answered the stranger in a clear ringing voice. "I will abide by the wager, as must you."

At a signal he and the ogre sprang forward on the course. Mudjee Monedo ran well, but the stranger soon outstripped him. So swiftly he ran his feet scarce seemed to touch the ground. The light played about him, and his feathers streamed behind him in the wind. Never had the ogre been so easily outrun. Sooner than usual he was obliged to turn himself into a wolf or he would have been left too far behind. In that shape he tore past the warrior, but as he passed the stranger heard a wheezing in his throat and knew that the birch bud was still there.

A low moan sounded from the crowd of watching Indians on the hill-side as they saw the grey wolf leading in the race. But the next moment, the moan changed to a shout of surprise. The strange warrior had changed himself into a partridge; he rose swiftly in the air, flew past over Mudjee Monedo, and lighted on the course far ahead of him. Then he resumed his natural form and again ran forward.

The ogre did not know what had happened. He heard the shout and the whirr of wings above him, and now he saw the stranger far ahead. He was very much surprised, but again he used his magic and turned himself into a deer. With long leaps and bounds he overtook and passed beyond the running warrior.

Again there was a whirr of wings. The partridge flew past overhead, and a mocking voice cried in the ogre's ear, "Mudjee Monedo, is this the best you can do?" A moment later the ogre saw the stranger once more far ahead, and running as lightly and gracefully as ever.

The charred stump was passed and Mudjee Monedo's heart began to beat hard against his sides. Never had he had to strive so hard. For the third time he used his magic, and turned himself into his third and last form, that of a buffalo. It was in this shape that he generally won the race. With his great shaggy head down, his eyes as red as blood and his tongue lolling from his mouth, the ogre thundered past the stranger.

Once again there was a whirr of wings. The partridge rose from the ground and flew past over the head of the straining buffalo. "Mudjee Monedo," he called from above, "is this the best you can do? I fear you will lose the wager."

With despair the ogre saw that the stranger had once more flown far ahead of him, and was now almost within reach of the goal-post. Suddenly stopping, Mudjee Monedo resumed his natural form. "Hold! hold!" he called to the warrior. "A word with you."

The stranger gave a mocking laugh. Springing forward he laid his hand upon the goal-post, and a mighty shout burst from the watching people on the hill. Then a stillness fell upon them. In silence they watched the ogre as he slowly went forward toward the goal-post.

As he drew near the stranger Mudjee Monedo tried to smile, but his pale lips trembled. "It was all a joke," he muttered. "You will spare my life, as I would have spared yours. You run well and we must have many races together."

"Wretch!" cried the stranger. "What was the wager? Life against life; the loser pays the forfeit."

Swift as lightning he caught up the club that hung from the goal-post, and with one blow he struck the ogre to the earth. Then again a great shout arose from the people, and like a stream they flowed down from the hill-side and gathered around the warrior.

For a time there was great rejoicing. Fires were lighted and a great feast made. When night came and the stranger went back to his lodge a vast crowd followed him. It was growing dark, but suddenly a pale light shone about the warrior. He turned to them, and as they looked at his face they suddenly knew it was no human warrior who stood before them, but the Good Genius, Minno Monedo. Silent and in awe they drew back from him. He motioned them to leave him, and they obeyed him, still in awe and silence.

After they had all gone Minno Monedo turned to his wife and took her by the hand. "The time has now come," he said, "when I must return to the Spirit-land. It is for you to choose whether you will come with me or stay here with your own people. Which shall it be?"

"I will go with you," answered the wife.

So it was; she and the Good Genius disappeared from the earth, and her tribe saw them no more.

For a while her mother grieved for her, but Manedowa grew up strong and brave, and in time brought home a wife who bore him many children.

Grass grew over the course where the ogre had run his races; his lodge fell into ruins, but still around the camp-fires the Indians tell the story of Minno Monedo, and of how he came to save their tribe from Mudjee Monedo.

Week One:

THE KING OF THE BUFFALOES

Native North American Legend

RETOLD BY KATHARINE PYLE

A lame Indian and his daughter once lived on the edge of a lonely forest, apart from any tribe or village. The Indian, whose name was Agodaguada, was a great hunter and fisher in spite of his lameness. Every day he went off into the forest, and while he was away his daughter, Iola, took care of the lodge and did the cooking.

They would have been very contented there if it had not been for a herd of buffaloes that lived on the other side of the forest. The king of this herd was a magician. He had seen Iola once as she was gathering wood in the forest, and had fallen in love with her, for she was very beautiful. Agodaguada often came upon him hiding in the bushes near the hut or heard him bellowing down at a stream nearby. Agodaguada cautioned his daughter never to leave the lodge while he was away, for he feared the buffalo might seize her and carry her off.

He himself was tormented by the ungainly beasts. They muddied the streams where he fished and drove away the game by their bellowing. Gradually he was obliged to go farther and farther from the lodge to find deer or fish. Often as he sat quietly watching for game a hoarse voice would begin to sing at him from behind the bushes or rocks:

"You lame mannikin,
Don't you think it a sin

To pen up your daughter?
—Say, Agodaguada—
To shut up your daughter,
Don't you think it a sin?"

Sometimes he aimed an arrow or a stone at the place from which the voice sounded, and then a great dark body would go lumbering and crashing away through the forest, and Agodaguada would know that it was one of the buffaloes that had followed him.

One day, when Agodaguada was far from home, his daughter climbed up on top of the lodge, and sat there to comb her hair, for it was very long. Every now and then she stopped to listen and look about her, to make sure there was no danger.

For a long time, all was silent except for the singing of the birds. She finished combing her hair and was just about to go down into the lodge when suddenly a great noise arose, a crashing of underbrush and thundering of hoofs. The herd of buffaloes, with the king at their head, was charging down upon the hut. Iola had no time to move before she felt the logs breaking away beneath her. They were scattered this way and that like straws. In another moment Iola found herself seated on the back of the king of buffaloes. She was being carried swiftly away through the forest, while the lodge lay in ruins behind them.

On and on went the buffalo, until at last, in the deepest and darkest part of the forest, he paused and allowed Iola to slip from his back.

This was the spot where he and his followers had their camp, and it was here he intended to keep Iola until she consented to become his wife. He spoke to her in the softest voice he could manage, telling her that this was to be her home, but Iola would not look at him, nor answer. She only turned away, wringing her hands and weeping bitterly.

But the buffalo king was not discouraged. He had the power to take the shape of a man when he chose, and it was in this shape that he meant to woo her and win her to be his wife. And this he had no doubt of being able to do before long.

Meanwhile Agodaguada had been trying to fish, but he found his enemies more tormenting than ever. Their hoarse voices sang after him wherever he went:

"You lame mannikin,
Don't you think it a sin
To shut up your daughter?
—Say, Agodaguada—
To shut up your daughter?
Do you think she is in?
Are you sure she is in?"

As Agodaguada listened, he became thoughtful. He rolled up his line and started back through the forest toward the lodge. As he came near his home, he quickened his steps. He noticed that the small trees and underbrush had been trampled down as though a great herd had passed that way. Presently he began to run, and he was still running when he broke into the open where his lodge had stood. But the lodge was there no longer. Instead, he saw only the ruins that the buffaloes had left behind them. Iola was gone.

Agodaguada did not at once follow the enemy, however. He ran to the ruins and began tearing the logs aside and burrowing under them. Presently he gave a cry of joy and drew out from beneath them an old worn pouch of deerskin. From this pouch he took a pair of moccasins and put them on his feet. They were magic moccasins and were Agodaguada's greatest treasure. And now he was ready to follow Iola and save her from the buffaloes.

It was not hard to trace the way they had gone. The herd had left a broad track of broken trees and branches through the dark forest.

The magic moccasins leaped a hundred yards at each step. They carried Agodaguada along faster than a bird can fly. The buffaloes had gone at full speed and had had the start of him by several hours, but so swiftly he went that by twilight he found himself close to their camp.

Here he slipped the moccasins from his feet. As silently as a snake he crawled past the other wigwams toward the lodge of the king.

As he came near it he heard the sound of a flute, and soon he was close enough to look inside and see who was playing. It was the king himself. He had taken his human form and was playing upon his flute a love song to Iola, but as a man he was even more hideous than he was as a buffalo.

Iola sat with her back turned toward him. She looked very sad. Her head was sunk on her breast, and she took no notice of his love song or of his languishing glances.

Suddenly Iola started. From the thicket outside had sounded the whistle of a partridge. It was the whistle her father always gave as he came near home after a day of hunting. The buffalo, playing on his flute, had heard nothing.

Iola sat still a few moments longer, and then she rose. "I will go down to the spring," she said, "and fetch the water for the cooking."

When the buffalo heard her say this he was filled with joy. He took it as a sign that she was now ready to live with him in his wigwam and be his wife. Believing this, he was quite willing to allow her to go down to the spring by herself.

Iola stepped outside, and as soon as her father saw her alone there, he rose up from among the bushes. His magic moccasins were once more upon his feet. He motioned her to follow. "Quick!" he whispered. As soon as they were clear of the bushes Agodaguada lifted his daughter in his arms and leaped away with her through the forest.

In the lodge the buffalo waited for Iola a long time. Sometimes he listened for her footsteps, and sometimes he played upon his flute. At last he began to grow suspicious and went out to look for her. Everywhere he looked and hunted, and at last he came to where her father had hidden in the bushes, and there he saw the marks Agodaguada had made as he had leaped away with Iola in his arms.

Then the buffalo knew he had been tricked. With a bellow of rage, he called his herd together and started after Iola and her father.

Agodaguada had already gone some distance, but his daughter weighed him down, and the moccasins could not move as swiftly as when they had only himself to carry. He had only just reached the edge of the forest when he heard the buffaloes behind him. They had caught sight of him. The king gave a bellow of triumph. But now Agodaguada was out of the forest and leaping swiftly over an open plain. The whole herd were thundering after him at full speed, but just as the leader reached him Agodaguada leaped aside. Before the buffaloes could stop themselves, they had charged on past him.

They turned and again rushed at him. But suddenly a flight of arrows darkened the air. Several buffaloes fell dead upon the plain, and the king was wounded. These arrows were shot by a band of hunters who had come to this plain in search of game and had hidden themselves in a thicket. From there they had seen Agodaguada race with the buffaloes.

Though the king was wounded, he would still have pursued Agodaguada, but his followers had turned tail and were fleeing back into the forest. He stood pawing the earth and frothing until another arrow struck him, and then, bellowing with rage, he turned and followed his herd.

He did not stop at the camp, however. He was so full of anger and chagrin that he went on and on until he reached the wide plains of the West, where he had never been seen or heard of before.

But Agodaguada joined the band of hunters who had saved him, and Iola was married to their young chief and lived happily with him in his lodge for ever after.

Illustration by Frederic Remington for Francis Parkman in *The Oregon Trail: Sketches of Prairie and Rocky-Mountain Life* (Boston: Little, Brown, and Company, 1909).

Week One:

THE BUFFALO TRAIL

Deeply the buffalo trod it
    Beating it barren as brass;
  Now the soft rain-fingers sod it,
    Green to the crest of the pass.
Backward it slopes into history;
Forward it lifts into mystery.
      Here is but wind in the grass.

  Backward the millions assemble,
    Bannered with dust overhead,
  Setting the prairie a-tremble
    Under the might of their tread.
Forward the sky-line is glistening
And to the reach of our listening
      Drifts not a sound from the dead.

  Quick, or the swift seasons fade it!
    Look on his works while they show.
  This is the bison. He made it.
    Thus say the old ones who know.
This is the bison—a-pondering
Vague as the prairie wind wandering
      Over the green or the snow.
        CHARLES BADGER CLARK
          (1883–1957)

"The air was full of shining drops of water and shining fish." Illustration by Alice Corbin Henderson for Marion Foster Washburne in *Indian Legends* (Chicago: Rand McNally, c. 1915).

Week Two:

How the Bear Family Got Its Name

Native North American Legend

RETOLD BY MARION FOSTER WASHBURNE

Upon the banks of the broad Ogechee River there once stood a little Indian village. The people who lived there were prosperous and happy. There were fish in the river and game in the forest, and no one lacked for anything.

My great-grandmother's name was Bear. She was very proud of the fact, and often talked to us about it. We boys must be brave hunters and skillful fishers, because the men of the Bear family had always been great hunters and skillful fishers. The girls must sew well, and especially know how to dry meat and berries, for so the women of the Bear family had always done. On rainy evenings, when we all sat around the lodge fire, we would say to the old woman, nodding in the smoke, "Grandmother, tell us: How do we come to be called Bears? Are any of the wild bears in the mountains relatives of ours?"

And then she would tell us this story:

"Long ago there was a large Indian village on the banks of a river. In it lived an orphan boy who had no special home. However, all were kind to him; he was welcome in every lodge. He would live in one for a week or two, and then, someone inviting him, would live in another. But no one person had charge of him.

"One day, late in the fall, when winter was drawing near and the leaves had all fallen to the ground, this little boy went to the woods to gather berries. Many had been there before him, laying in supplies for the winter, and he had to go far before he found any fruit. The wind-stripped trees, letting in plenty of sunlight, made the woods look open and harmless, so he wandered farther than he knew.

"When it began to grow dark and cold he turned to go home. All about him stretched trees and trees — and yet more trees — as far as he could see. Under foot the earth was deep in leaves. He could not find his own trail; he did not know where the village was. He was lost in the woods, on the edge of night and of winter.

"Night fell. He shivered, and cried for the mother he had never known. At last, through his tears, he saw a light shining. He dashed his hand across his eyes. The light still shone. He hurried toward it. Yes, there was a lodge.

"Within, by the fire, sat a woman and two boys. The woman told him to enter. The boys danced around him, for joy that they had a new comrade. He was given dried berries and dried meat to eat, and lay down between the boys to sleep.

"In the morning he looked with new eyes on the people who had been so kind to him. Then he saw that it was not an old woman who had taken him in, but a she-bear, and that the two boys were two cubs. However, they knew how to play as well as any boy, and so the three romped together until the mother bear chased them out of the lodge— or the den, as it now showed itself to be—to play in the open air where the noise would not split her ears. The she-bear was very kind to the little boy who had sought her shelter. She fed him when she fed her cubs, and he was warm and comfortable. He stayed with the bears all winter.

"Back in the village the people missed him, after a day or so; but although they searched for him they could not find him. They gave him up for lost.

"At last spring came, and the whole village was astir. This was the time of year when the smelts came up the river and into all the little fresh-water streams to lay their eggs. They came in crowds, and both bears and Indians went to catch them.

"And so the three romped together until the mother bear chased them out of the lodge."
Illustration by Alice Corbin Henderson for Marion Foster Washburne in *Indian Legends*
(Chicago: Rand McNally, c. 1915).

"Sometimes the Indians shot the bears while they were busy catching fish, and thus got good fur and meat. This was the good luck one hunter expected as he came to a little stream in the depths of the woods, and saw the tracks of a bear and two cubs. They showed plainly in the springtime mud. But how was this? Beside them were the marks of a boy's naked feet.

"'Here is a strange thing,' said the hunter to himself. 'I will watch and see what more happens.' He hid himself in some bushes on the bank.

"Presently he heard the crackling of broken twigs, then the thud-thud of heavy steps, and looking out he saw a she-bear coming down to the opposite bank of the brook. With her were two cubs and the missing boy. He was talking to the cubs as he pattered along beside them. The man could hear and understand all he said, and the boy seemed to understand all the cubs said; but to the man the sound the cubs made was just an unmeaning animal mutter.

"When she got down to the brook the mother bear waded in and sat down in the water, her broad haunches filling up much of the bed of the brook, and her forepaws spread out on either side. Thus she made a dam of herself, and the fish, swimming hastily up the stream, in a blind hurry to lay their eggs and be off home again, dashed full against her. She threw them out on the bank with her paws. Behind her stood the little boy, his brown legs wide apart, catching those that escaped her. The two cubs danced about on the banks, stuffing themselves full of fish.

"The old bear was having fine sport.

"'There they come! There they come!' she shouted, and splashed like mad. The air was full of shining drops of water and shining fish, curving from her paws to the bank. She threw them in a fast glittering shower—threw them faster than a fisherman throws them from a net.

"The hunter went home and told his people what he had seen. They held a council. It was hard to think how they could get the boy without enraging the old bear, who might hurt him if she were made desperate. Many pipes they smoked over it. At last they decided on a plan.

"Next day toward sunset—for the fish come up most wildly as the dark draws near—twenty strong men set out for the brook in the depths of the woods. They went a long way around, so as not to cross the bear's tracks or let her get scent of them. They hid themselves in the bushes on each side of the brook.

"The old bear swung into view, her cubs lumbering after her. Beside them ran the little boy, naked, and light on his feet. To the edge of the brook they came; in plunged the old bear. Splash! the water wet the leaves far off as she flopped down.

"The boy stood behind her, and, spreading out her paws, she began to fish. The water rushed, the little bears danced, the fish flew out of the water and beat the ground with their tails. The old bear slapped fast, shouting and growling for joy. How could she hear the hunters closing in on her?

"They made a great circle on both sides of the brook. They made a narrower circle—narrower yet—they were upon her. They seized her boy, his brown body wet and slippery.

"The old bear rose on her hind legs, the water spiking her fur and dropping off the points into the brook again. She growled in her throat. Red and angry her little eyes were. She turned them on the boy she had nursed, and their look changed. After all, these were his own people. That is what she must have thought, for she did not fight. She dropped to her four legs, hung her head, and shambled off. She went slowly. She was not afraid; and no one hurt her.

"Once she stopped and looked at the little boy. He was struggling like a wild thing, biting and scratching as his brothers in the den had taught him to do. The bear hung her head again, but not so low. She looked to see if her own two cubs were close by her side, and together they disappeared into the woods.

"Eh, that was a wild boy they had on their hands! He had not forgotten how to talk, but he liked his food raw and he liked to go without clothes. All over his little naked body small black hairs were sprouting.

"But every one was so kind to him that at last he grew tame and quiet. He became a mighty hunter, but he would never hunt bears. Neither would he ever allow the old mother bear or her two cubs to be hurt. Often, in the winters, he carried food to their den. He was called the Bear, and we, who belonged to his family, who are of his blood, are called Bears to this day. All the Bears in the woods and in the mountains are our friends, and never do we hurt them."

Week Two:

The Boy Who Set a Snare for the Sun

Native North American Legend

Retold by Cornelius Mathews

At the time when the animals reigned in the earth, they had killed all the people but a girl and her little brother, and these two were living in fear, in an out-of-the-way place. The boy was a perfect little pigmy, and never grew beyond the size of a mere infant; but the girl increased with her years, so that the task of providing food and shelter fell wholly upon her. She went out daily to get wood for the lodge-fire, and she took her little brother with her that no mishap might befall him; for he was too little to leave alone. A big bird, of a mischievous disposition, might have flown away with him. She made him a bow and arrows, and said to him one day, "My little brother, I will leave you behind where I have been gathering the wood; you must hide yourself, and you will soon see the snow-birds come and pick the worms out of the logs which I have piled up. Shoot one of them and bring it home."

He obeyed her, and tried his best to kill one, but he came home unsuccessful. His sister told him that he must not despair but try again the next day.

She accordingly left him at the gathering-place of the wood and returned to the lodge. Toward night-fall she heard his little footsteps crackling through the snow, and he hurried in and threw down, with an air of triumph, one of the birds which he had killed. "My sister," said he, "I wish you to skin it, and stretch the skin, and when I have killed more, I will have a coat made out of them."

"But what shall we do with the body?" said she; for they had always up to that time lived upon greens and berries.

"Cut it in two," he answered, "and season our pottage with one half of it at a time."

It was their first dish of game, and they relished it greatly.

The boy kept on in his efforts, and in the course of time he killed ten birds—out of the skins of which his sister made him a little coat: being very small, he had a very pretty coat, and a bird skin to spare.

"Sister," said he, one day, as he paraded up and down before the lodge, enjoying his new coat, and fancifying himself the greatest little fellow in the world—as he was, for there was no other beside him—"My sister, are we really alone in the world, or are we playing at it? Is there nobody else living? And, tell me, was all this great broad earth and this huge big sky made for a little boy and girl like you and me?"

She told him, by no means; there were many folks very unlike a harmless girl and boy, such as they were, who lived in a certain other quarter of the earth, who had killed off all of their kinsfolk; and that if he would live blameless and not endanger his life, he must never go where they were. This only served to inflame the boy's curiosity; and he soon after took his bow and arrows and went in that direction. After walking a long time and meeting no one, he became tired, and stretched himself upon a high green knoll where the day's warmth had melted off the snow.

It was a charming place to lie upon, and he fell asleep; and, while sleeping, the sun beat so hot upon him that it not only singed his bird-skin coat, but it so shrivelled and shrunk and tightened it upon the little boy's body, as to wake him up.

When he felt how the sun had seared and the mischief its fiery beams had played with the coat he was so proud of, he flew into a great passion, and berated the sun in a terrible way for a little boy no higher than a man's knee, and he vowed fearful things against it.

"Do not think you are too high," said he; "I shall revenge myself. Oh, sun! I will have you for a plaything yet."

On coming home, he gave an account of his misfortune to his sister, and bitterly bewailed the spoiling of his new coat. He would not eat—not so much as a single berry. He lay down as one that fasts; nor did he move nor change his manner of lying for ten full days, though his sister strove to prevail on him to rise. At the end of ten days he turned over, and then he lay full ten days on the other side.

When he got up, he was very pale, but very resolute too. He bade his sister make a snare, for, he informed her, that he meant to catch the sun. She said she had nothing; but after awhile she brought forward a deer's sinew which the father had left, and which she soon made into a string suitable for a noose. The moment she showed it to him he was quite wroth, and told her that would not do, and directed her to find something else. She said she had nothing—nothing at all. At last she thought of the bird-skin that was left over when the coat was made; and this she wrought into a string. With this the little boy was more vexed than before. "The sun has had enough of my bird-skins," he said; "find something else." She went out of the lodge saying to herself, "Was there ever so obstinate a boy?" She did not dare to answer this time that she had nothing. Luckily she thought of her own beautiful hair, and pulling some of it from among her locks, she quickly braided it into a cord, and, returning, she handed it to her brother. The moment his eye fell upon this jet-black braid he was delighted. "This will do," he said; and he immediately began to run it back and forth through his hands as swiftly as he could; and as he drew it forth, he tried its strength. He said again, "this will do;" and winding it in a glossy coil about his shoulders, he set out a little after midnight. His object was to catch the sun before he rose. He fixed his snare firmly on a spot just where the sun must strike the land as it rose above the earth; and sure enough, he caught the sun, so that it was held fast in the cord and did not rise.

The animals who ruled the earth were immediately put into great commotion. They had no light; and they ran to and fro, calling out to each other, and inquiring what had happened. They summoned a council to debate upon the matter, and an old dormouse, suspecting where the trouble lay, proposed that someone should be appointed to go and cut the cord. This was a bold thing to undertake, as the rays of the sun could not fail to burn whoever should venture so near to them.

At last the venerable dormouse himself undertook it, for the very good reason that no one else would. At this time the dormouse was the largest animal in the world. When he stood up, he looked like a mountain. It made haste to the place where the sun lay ensnared, and as it came nearer and nearer, its back began to smoke and burn with the heat, and the whole top of his huge bulk was turned in a very short time to enormous heaps of ashes. It succeeded, however, in cutting the cord with its teeth and freeing the sun, which rolled up again, as round and beautiful as ever, into the wide blue sky. But the dormouse—or blind woman as it is called—was shrunk away to a very small size; and that is the reason why it is now one of the tiniest creatures upon the earth.

The little boy returned home when he discovered that the sun had escaped his snare and devoted himself entirely to hunting. "If the beautiful hair of my sister would not hold the sun fast, nothing in the world could," he said. "He was not born, a little fellow like himself, to look after the sun. It required one greater and wiser than he was to regulate that." And he went out and shot ten more snow-birds; for in this business he was very expert; and he had a new bird-skin coat made, which was prettier than the one he had worn before.

Week Two:
THE PLEIADES

By day you cannot see the sky
For it is up so very high.
You look and look, but it's so blue
That you can never see right through.

But when night comes it is quite plain,
And all the stars are there again.
They seem just like old friends to me,
I've known them all my life you see.

There is the dipper first, and there
Is Cassiopeia in her chair,
Orion's belt, the Milky Way,
And lots I know but cannot say.

One group looks like a swarm of bees,
Papa says they're the Pleiades;
But I think they must be the toy
Of some nice little angel boy.

Perhaps his jackstones which to-day
He has forgot to put away,
And left them lying on the sky
Where he will find them bye and bye.

I wish he'd come and play with me.
We'd have such fun, for it would be
A most unusual thing for boys
To feel that they had stars for toys!

AMY LOWELL
(1874–1925)

Week Three:

THE FROGS AND THE CRANE

Sioux Folk Tale

RETOLD BY CHARLES A. EASTMAN AND

ELAINE GOODALE EASTMAN

SECOND EVENING

Again the story-hour is come, and the good old wife of the legend-teller has made her poor home as warm and pleasant as may be, in expectation of their guests. She is proud of her husband's honorable position as the village teacher, and makes all the children welcome, as they arrive, with her shrill-voiced, cheerful greeting:

"Han, han; sit down, sit down; that is right, that is very right, my grandchild!"

To-night the Humming-bird has come leading by the hand her small brother, who stumbles along in his fringed, leathern leggings and handsomely beaded moccasins, his chubby, solemn face finished off with two long, black braids tied with strips of otter-skin. As he is inclined to be restless and to talk out of season, she keeps him close beside her.

"It is cold to-night!" he pipes up suddenly when all is quiet. "Why do we not listen to these stories in the warm summer-time, elder sister?"

"Hush, my little brother!" Tanagela reproves him with a frightened look. "Have you never heard that if the old stories are told in summer, the snakes will creep into our beds?" she whispers fearfully.

"That is true, my granddaughter," assents the old man. "Yet we may tell a legend of summer days to comfort the heart of the small brother!"

THE FROGS AND THE CRANE

In the heart of the woods there lay a cool, green pond. The shores of the pond were set with ranks of tall bulrushes that waved crisply in the wind, and in the shallow bays there were fleets of broad water lily leaves. Among the rushes and reeds and in the quiet water there dwelt a large tribe of Frogs.

On every warm night of spring, the voices of the Frogs arose in a cheerful chorus. Some voices were low and deep—these were the oldest and wisest of the Frogs; at least, they were old enough to have learned wisdom. Some were high and shrill, and these were the voices of the little Frogs who did not like to be reminded of the days when they had tails and no legs.

"Kerrump! kerrump! I'm chief of this pond!" croaked a very large bullfrog, sitting in the shade of a water lily leaf.

"Kerrump! kerrump! I'm chief of this pond!" replied a hoarse voice from the opposite bank.

"Kerrump! kerrump! I'm chief of this pond!" boasted a third old Frog from the furthest shore of the pond.

Now a long-legged white Crane was standing near by, well hidden by the coarse grass that grew at the water's edge. He was very hungry that evening, and when he heard the deep voice of the first Bullfrog he stepped briskly up to him and made a quick pass under the broad leaf with his long, cruel bill. The old Frog gave a frightened croak, and kicked violently in his efforts to get away, while over the quiet pond, splash! splash! went the startled little Frogs into deep water.

The Crane almost had him, when something cold and slimy wound itself about one of his legs. He drew back for a second, and the Frog got safely away! But the Crane did not lose his dinner after all, for about his leg was curled a large black water snake, and that made a fair meal.

Now he rested awhile on one leg, and listened. The first Frog was silent, but from the opposite bank the second Frog croaked boastfully:

"Kerrump! kerrump! I'm chief of this pond!"

The Crane began to be hungry again. He went round the pond without making any noise, and pounced upon the second Frog, who was sitting up in plain sight, swelling his chest with pride, for he really thought now that he was the sole chief of the pond.

The Crane's head and most of his long neck disappeared under the water, and all over the pond the little Frogs went splash! splash! into the deepest holes to be out of the way.

Just as he had the Frog by one hind leg, the Crane saw something that made him let go, flap his broad wings and fly awkwardly away to the furthest shore. It was a mink, with his slender brown body and wicked eyes, and he had crept very close to the Crane, hoping to seize him at his meal! So the second Frog got away too; but he was so dreadfully frightened that he never spoke again.

After a long time the Crane got over his fright and he became very hungry once more. The pond had been still so long that many of the Frogs were singing their pleasant chorus, and above them all there boomed the deep voice of the third and last Bullfrog, saying:

"Kerrump! kerrump! I'm chief of this pond!"

The Crane stood not far from the boaster, and he determined to silence him once for all. The next time he began to speak, he had barely said "Kerrump!" when the Crane had him by the leg. He croaked and struggled in vain, and in another moment he would have gone down the Crane's long throat.

But just then a Fox crept up behind the Crane and seized *him*! The Crane let go the Frog and was carried off screaming into the woods for the Fox's supper. So the third Frog got away; but he was badly lamed by the Crane's strong bill, and he never dared to open his mouth again.

It is not a wise thing to boast too loudly.

"He came one day upon a man clad in scarlet sitting on the side of a rocky hill tying stones to his feet." Illustration by Marcia Lane Foster for Cyrus Macmillan in *Canadian Fairy Tales* (New York: Dodd, Mead and Co., 1922).

Week Three:

Great Heart and the Three Tests

Canadian Fairy Tale

RETOLD BY CYRUS MACMILLAN

Somewhere near the sea in olden times a boy was living with his father and mother. He had no brothers or sisters. His father was a great hunter and the boy inherited something of his power, for he was always very successful in the killing of game. And his mother said, "Some day he will be a great man, for before his birth a vision came to me in the night and told me that my son would win wide fame. And fairy gifts were laid by the fairies in his cradle." And his father, listening to her boasting, said, "Time will tell; time will tell; but if he is to be a great man it is his own deeds and not your boasting that must prove it." As the boy grew up he became strangely beautiful and he had great strength. And his father said, "It is time he set out to seek his fortune. I was in the forest doing for myself when I was no older than he." And his mother said, "Wait a little and be not so impatient. He is yet young and there is yet much time." So the boy remained at home a while longer.

Now it happened that far away in a distant village there lived a young girl of very great beauty and grace. Her father had been a great Chief, but he was now dead. Her mother too was dead, and she was all alone in the world. But her parents had left her vast lands and a great store of goods and many servants, and because of her treasures and her great beauty she had many suitors. But she was not easily pleased by men and on all who came to seek her hand she imposed severe feats of skill to test their sincerity and their worth. She was carefully guarded by an old woman and many servants who kept troublesome and meddlesome people away.

Soon the fame of the girl's wealth and beauty spread through all the land. It reached the sea coast village where the young man dwelt. His father thought to himself, "Here is a good chance for my son to prove his worth." So he called his boy to him and said, "It is time you were setting out to seek your fortune in the world and to find a wife, for your spring-time is passing and your summer of life will soon be here, and before you know it your autumn will be upon you and your winter will be near. There is no time to lose. Seek out the beautiful girl of the rich treasures in the distant inland village and try to win her as your wife." And his mother gave him the fairy gifts which had been laid in his cradle at his birth, and he said good-bye to his parents and set out on his long journey. He had no misgivings, for he was very vain of his beauty and he was sure, too, of his strength.

As he traveled inland he came one day upon a man clad in scarlet sitting on the side of a rocky hill tying stones to his feet. "Hello," he said to the man, "why are you tying these heavy rocks to your ankles?" "I am a hunter," replied the man, "but when I follow the deer I run so fast that I am soon far in front of them instead of behind them, and I am putting heavy weights on my feet so that I will not run so rapidly." "You are indeed a wonderful man," said the boy; "but I am alone and I need a companion. Let us go along together." "Who are you?" said the man. "I am Lad of the Great Heart," said the boy, "and I can do great deeds and I can win for you great treasure." So the Scarlet Runner went along with him.

Towards evening when they were now far inland, they came to a large lake. Among the trees on the fringe of the lake a large fat man was lying flat on his stomach with his mouth in the water drinking as hard as he could. For some time they watched him, but still he drank and the lake grew smaller and smaller and still his thirst was not quenched. They laughed at such a strange sight, and as they approached him the boy said, "Hello! Why do you lie there drinking so much water?" "Oh," answered the fat man, "there are times when I cannot get enough water to drink. When I have drunk this lake dry I shall still be thirsty." "Who are you?" asked the boy. "I am Man of the Great Thirst," said the fat man. "That is well," said Great Heart, "we two need a third companion. We can do great deeds and we can win for you great treasure." So the three went along together.

They had not gone far when they came to a wide open plain where they saw a man walking along with his face raised upwards, peering at the sky. He moved along rapidly and seemed to find his way without his eyes, for he gazed steadily at the heavens. "Hello," said Great Heart as the sky-gazer rushed past him and almost knocked him over, "what are you looking at so intently?" "Oh," said the man, "I have shot an arrow into the sky and I am waiting for it to fall. It has gone so far that it will be some time before it drops." "Who are you?" asked the boy. "I am the Far-Darter," said the sky-gazer. "We three need a fourth companion," said the boy. "We can do great deeds and win for you much treasure. Come along with us." So the four went along together.

They had gone but a short distance across the plain to the edge of a forest when they came upon a man lying down at full length with his head upon his hand. The edge of his hand was on the ground and it was half closed around his ear, which rested upon it. As he saw the four men approaching him he placed a finger of his other hand upon his lips and signaled to them to keep quiet. "Hello," said Great Heart in a whisper, "what are you doing there with your ear to the ground?" "I am listening to the plants growing far away in the forest," he answered. "There is a beautiful flower I wish to find, and I am trying to hear it breathing so that I may go and get it. Aha! I hear it now." So saying he rose from the ground. The boy said, "Who are you?" "I am Keen Ears," said the listener. "We four need another companion," said Great Heart. "We can do great deeds and win for you much treasure. Come along with us." So the four men and the boy went along together, Keen Ears, and Scarlet Runner, and Far Darter, and Man of the Great Thirst, and Lad of the Great Heart. Then Great Heart unfolded to the others his plan to win the beautiful girl who lived with her treasures in the distant village. And they gladly agreed to help him in his dangerous undertaking.

When they reached the village, the people were all very curious when they saw the five strangers. They marveled at Great Heart's beauty. But when they heard that he wished to marry the daughter of the former Chief they shook their heads gravely and said, "It will never be. She places hard conditions on all who seek her hand. He who fails in the tests is doomed to death. Many suitors have tried and failed and died." But Great Heart was not alarmed, and with his four companions he went to the girl's home. The old woman who guarded her met him at the door and he made known his wishes. She laughed scornfully when she saw his great beauty, and she said, "You look more like a girl than like a warrior. You cannot endure the tests." But the young man insisted on making the trials.

The old woman said, "If you fail in the tests you will die," and Great Heart said, "It is so agreed." Then the woman said, "If you wish to win the maiden you must first push away this great rock from before her window. It keeps the sunlight from her in the mornings." Then Great Heart, calling to his aid the fairy gifts of his cradle, placed his shoulder against the huge stone which rose higher than the house, and he pushed with all his strength. With a mighty crash it rolled down the hill and broke into millions of pieces. The bits of rock flew all over the earth so great was the fall, and the little pebbles and stones that came from it are seen throughout the world to this day. The sunlight streamed in at the window, and the maiden knew that the first test had been successfully passed by a suitor.

Then came the second test. The old woman and her servants brought great quantities of food and drink and bade the strangers consume it all at one meal. They were very hungry, for they had eaten nothing all day and they easily ate up the food. But when Great Heart saw the great barrels of water, his spirits sank, and he said, "I fear I am beaten." But Man of the Great Thirst said, "Not so fast, my friend. The spell of great stomach-burning is again upon me. I am very dry as if there was a fire in my belly. Give me a chance to drink." He went from barrel to barrel and in a twinkling he had drained them all of every drop. And the people wondered greatly.

But there was still another test. "You must have one of your party run a race," said the old woman to Great Heart. And she brought out a man who had never been beaten in running. "Who is your choice of runners?" she asked; "he must race with this man, and if he wins you may have the maiden for your wife and all the treasure with her, for this is the final test. But if he loses the race you shall die." Great Heart called Scarlet Runner to the mark and told the old woman that this was the man selected. Then he untied the rocks from the runner's feet, and when all was ready the race began. The course lay far across the plains for many miles until the runners should pass from sight, and back again to the starting point. The two runners kept together for some distance, talking together in a friendly way as they ran. When they had passed from sight of the village the maiden's runner said, "Now we are out of sight of the village. Let us rest here a while on this grassy bank, for the day is hot." The Scarlet Runner agreed to this and they both stretched out on the grass. Now this was an old trick of the maiden's runner, who always won by craft rather than by speed. They had not lain down long on the grass when Scarlet Runner fell asleep under the hot sun, just as his rival had hoped. When the latter was sure that his rival was sound asleep, he set out for the village, running as fast as he could. The people soon saw their runner approaching far off on the plains, but there was no sign of the stranger, and they thought that the new suitor for the girl's hand had at last failed like all the others before him.

Great Heart was much puzzled when Scarlet Runner did not appear, and as he saw the maiden's runner coming nearer, he said, "What can have happened? I fear I am beaten." But Keen Ears threw himself flat on the ground and listened. "Scarlet Runner is asleep," he called; "I hear him snoring on the plains far away." And with his keen sense of sound he located the exact spot where the runner was lying. "I will soon wake him," said Far-Darter, as he fitted an arrow to his bow-string. The people all thought him mad, for they had never seen an arrow shot so great a distance beyond their sight. But Far-Darter was not dismayed. He quickly shot an arrow from his bow to the spot which Keen Ears had indicated. His aim was so true that the arrow hit Scarlet Runner on the nose and aroused him from his sleep. But when he rose to his feet he found that his rival was gone and he knew that he had been deceived. So in a great rage because of the trick and the pain in his nose, he set out for the village running like the wind. His rival had almost reached the end of the race, but by putting all his strength into his effort, Scarlet Runner quickly over-took him and passed him near the winning-post and won the race. And the people wondered greatly at these great deeds of the strangers.

Then the old woman said to Great Heart, "You have won the maiden as your wife, for you alone have succeeded in these tests." So the two were married with great ceremony. Great Heart gave much treasure to his companions, and they promised to help him always in his need. Then with his wife and her servants and her great store of goods he went back to his native village by the sea. His father and mother were glad to see him again and to hear of his success, and his mother said, "I told you he would win great fame because of the fairy gifts that were laid in his cradle at his birth." And they all lived together and were henceforth very happy.

Week Three:
THE SANDPIPER

Across the lonely beach we flit,
    One little sandpiper and I,
And fast I gather, bit by bit,
    The scattered driftwood, bleached and dry.
The wild waves reach their hands for it,
    The wild wind raves, the tide runs high,
As up and down the beach we flit, —
    One little sandpiper and I.

Above our heads the sullen clouds
    Scud, black and swift, across the sky;
Like silent ghosts in misty shrouds
    Stand out the white lighthouses high.
        Almost as far as eye can reach
            I see the close-reefed vessels fly,
        As fast we flit along the beach, —
            One little sandpiper and I.

I watch him as he skims along,
   Uttering his sweet and mournful cry;
He starts not at my fitful song,
   Nor flash of fluttering drapery.
He has no thought of any wrong,
   He scans me with a fearless eye;
Stanch friends are we, well tried and strong,
   The little sandpiper and I.

Comrade, where wilt thou be to-night,
   When the loosed storm breaks furiously?
My driftwood fire will burn so bright!
   To what warm shelter canst thou fly?
I do not fear for thee, though wroth
   The tempest rushes through the sky;
For are we not God's children both,
   Thou, little sandpiper, and I?

                    CELIA THAXTER
                    (1835–1894)

Week Four:

How Rabbit Deceived Fox

Canadian Fairy Tale

Retold by Cyrus Macmillan

ong ago in Indian days in Canada, when Rabbit worked for Glooskap as his forest guide, he was a great thief. He liked most of all to steal by moonlight, and he crept quietly into gardens and fields where Indian vegetables were growing, for he was very fond of cabbage and lettuce and beans. Not far from his home there lived alone an old widow woman who had no children. She could not hunt game because she was a woman, and she had never been trained to the chase, so she kept a little garden from which she made a good living. All day long from dawn until sunset she toiled hard, tilling her little garden, watering her vegetables and keeping them free from weeds. And she grew green cabbages and red carrots and yellow beans and big fat pumpkins and Indian corn, which she traded with Indian hunters in return for fish and meat. In this way she always had plenty of food, and she lived very well on good fare. But Rabbit, going his rounds one day, discovered her garden, although it was deep in the forest, and every night by moonlight or starlight he robbed it, and grew sleek and fat from the results of his thefts. And morning after morning the old widow woman found that many cabbages and carrots were missing and that much harm had been done to her plants. She had an idea that Rabbit was the pilferer, for she had heard that he was a great thief, but she was not very sure. She watched many nights, but she was never able to catch the robber, so stealthily did he come, and it was not easy to see him in the shadows. So she said to herself, "I will set up a scarecrow, a figure in the shape of a little man, and I will place it at my garden gate, and it will frighten away the robber, whoever he may be, for I must save my vegetables or I shall starve when the cold winter comes."

She picked from the spruce and the fir trees close by a great store of gum and balsam. This she formed into a figure in the shape of a little man. She made two eyes from glass beads that would shine like fire in the starlight, and a nose from a pine cone, and hair from the corn tassels and yellow moss. Then she placed the figure at the entrance to the garden where she knew the robber would come. "Now," she thought, "I will scare away the thief."

When night fell and the moon rose above the trees, Rabbit came along, as was his custom, to steal his nightly meal. As he came near the garden very softly, he saw in the moonlight what he thought was a man standing in the path by the garden gate. The moon hung low over the forest, and there was a thin grey mist on the earth, for it was near to autumn and the nights were already cool; and the figure of the little man looked larger than human in the misty light, and it cast a long black shadow like that of a giant on the grass. Rabbit was much afraid and he trembled like an aspen leaf, but he stood quiet behind a tree and watched the strange figure. For a long time he stood still and watched and listened. But the strange figure did not move, and not a sound did Rabbit hear but the chirp of a cricket. Then with great caution he came closer. But still the figure did not move. Then his fear left him and he grew bolder, for he was very hungry, and he could smell the vegetables and the wild honeysuckle in the still night air. So he walked bravely up to the little dummy man and said, "Get out of my way and let me pass." But the man did not move. Then Rabbit struck the man a sharp blow with his fist. But still the figure did not move. Rabbit's fist stuck fast in the gum and he could not pull it away. Then he struck out with his other fist, and it too, like the other, was held firm. "I shall kick you," said Rabbit in a rage. "Take that," and he struck out wildly with his foot. But his foot, like his fists, stuck fast. Then he kicked with the other foot, but that too was held in the gum. Rabbit was now very cross, and in his anger he said, "Now I shall bite you," but when he bit the little man, his teeth, like his feet and hands, stuck fast. Then he pushed with his body with all his might, hoping to knock the little man down, but his whole body stuck to the dummy figure.

He cried out loudly, for he was now beside himself with fear, and the old woman, when she heard his yells, came running out of her house. "Aha!" she said, "so you are the robber who has been stealing from my garden. I will rid the world of a pilfering pest, for I will kill you this very night." Then she pulled him away from the gum figure and put him in a strong bag and tied the mouth of the bag with a stout string. She left the bag on the path by the garden gate and went to look for her axe to kill Rabbit. While Rabbit lay there wondering how he was going to escape, Fox came prowling along. He stumbled over the bag, for he did not see it in the shadows, and he plunged forward headlong to the ground with a great thud. He got up and rained kicks upon the bag. He was mad because he had been tripped. He kicked poor Rabbit's back until Rabbit cried in pain. "Who are you in the bag?" asked Fox when he heard the cries. "I am your friend Rabbit," was the answer. "What are you doing, hiding in the bag?" asked Fox. Then Rabbit suddenly thought of a way of escape. He knew that Fox had long been looking for a wife, but that no one would have him as no one trusted him because his fame for treachery and slyness was so great. "I am not hiding," he said. "The old woman who owns this garden wants me to marry her grand-daughter, and when I refused to do it she caught me and shut me up in this bag; she has just gone to bring the girl from her house, for she is determined to make me marry her here in the moonlight this very night. I don't want to marry her, for she is very big and fat, and I am very small and lean." Then he cried "Boo-hoo-hoo" again, and Fox said, "I have been looking for a wife for a long time, and I like fat people. Let me get into the bag in your place, and I will marry the grand-daughter instead, for the old woman will not know me in the shadows." And Rabbit gladly agreed. Then Fox untied the bag and let Rabbit out and got into the bag himself, and Rabbit tied up the mouth of the bag and hurried away as quickly as he could.

"Then Fox untied the bag and let Rabbit out and got into the bag himself." Illustration by Marcia Lane Foster for Cyrus Macmillan in *Canadian Fairy Tales* (New York: Dodd, Mead and Co., 1922).

Soon the old woman came back, carrying her axe. She sharpened it on a stone and said, "Now I will kill you, and you will thieve no more in my garden. A poor woman must live untroubled by such pilfering rogues." When Fox heard these words and the sound of the stone upon the axe, he knew that he had been deceived by Rabbit, and when the old woman opened the bag he sprang nimbly out with a sudden bound and was away before she could catch him. He swore by the Starlight that he would have vengeance on Rabbit. All night long he searched for him and all the next day, but he could not find him. At last in the gathering twilight he came upon him in an open space in the forest, on the other side of a stream, eating his fill of wild vegetables. Fox tried to coax him across the stream to his side, for he himself was afraid of the water, but Rabbit would not go. "Why don't you eat some cheese?" said Rabbit; "there is a big round cheese in the stream." Fox looked into the stream where Rabbit pointed, and there he saw the reflection of the big round yellow moon. He thought it was a round cheese, and he plunged in after it, for he was very fond of cheese. Rabbit hoped he would be drowned, but the stream was shallow and Fox climbed out with no cheese and with only a bad fright and a wet coat for his pains. He was very cross, for he knew that Rabbit wished to do him harm, but he kept his anger to himself. Rabbit was still eating contentedly.

"What are you eating?" said Fox, trying to hold him in talk until he could think of a plan to catch him. "I am eating good ripe fruit," said Rabbit. "I am eating Indian melons." "Throw me one," said Fox, for he was hungry. Rabbit threw him a large round wild cucumber all covered with green prickles. "Swallow it whole at a mouthful," said Rabbit; "it is very good that way." It was night and the moon shone dimly through the trees, and Fox could not see what he was eating. He swallowed the cucumber at one gulp, as Rabbit had told him, but the prickles stuck in his throat and he almost choked to death. And while he was choking and spluttering and trying to cough up the cucumber, Rabbit ran away as fast as he could, laughing heartily to himself. Fox knew that he had been tricked again, and this time he swore he would kill Rabbit as soon as he could find him; he resolved that when next he saw him he would not give him a moment to live.

Rabbit hid among the dry underbrush all the next day. But when the day went down and the sky was red in the west and the wind was very still, he sat on a log, as was his custom, and played softly on his flute, for he was a great player on the Indian pipe. While he was playing, Fox suddenly came upon him unawares. Rabbit saw him watching him through the trees close at hand, but although taken by surprise, he was not to be outdone. Fox was just about to spring upon him when Rabbit said, "The Chief's daughter has just been married to a great warrior, and the wedding party will soon be along this way. They asked me to sit here and make music for them with my flute as they pass by. They have promised to pay me well, and they have invited me to the wedding feast. Come and join me and play too, and you will be well paid, and we will go to the wedding feast together and get good things to eat." Fox thought he would let Rabbit get the pay he had been promised, for he was a very greedy fellow; then he would rob him and kill him, and he would take his flute and go to the wedding feast alone, and his vengeance would then be complete. So he decided to let his anger cool for a little time. And he said, "I have no flute, and I cannot therefore make music; but I will sit with you to see the wedding guests go by." But Rabbit said, "Take my flute. I have another at home. I will go and get it, for there is yet time."

So Fox took the flute and began to play loudly, and Rabbit slipped hurriedly out of sight, pretending to go for his Indian pipe. But he resolved to make an end of Fox, for he feared for his own life, and instead of going home, he set the underbrush on fire. He kindled the fire at many places all around the log on which Fox sat. Fox could not hear the fire crackling because of the loud music of his flute, and he thought the light was but the bright light of the moon. And the fire was almost upon him before he knew that he was in danger. Then he tried to get away, but on all sides his escape was stopped by the flames and he could not find an opening. At last, in despair, to save his life, he jumped through the ring of fire. He escaped with his life, but his eyelids were singed, and his sleek black coat with its silver spots was scorched to a red-brown colour. He was in great pain. He concluded that Rabbit was too clever for him to cope with, and he resolved to leave him alone and to forego his revenge, for he was glad to get away with his life. But he decided never again to live on friendly terms with Rabbit. And since that night Rabbit and Fox have never hunted together. And to the present day the descendants of this Fox have red eyes and a red-brown coat, because Rabbit scorched their ancestor in the olden times.

Week Four:

How Raven Brought Fire to the Indians

Canadian Fairy Tale

Retold by Cyrus Macmillan

any ages ago when the world was still young, Raven and White Sea-gull lived near together in Canada, far in the north country on the shores of the Great Water in the west. They were very good friends and they always worked in harmony and they had much food and many servants in common. White Sea-gull knew no guile; he was always very open and frank and honest in his dealings with others. But Raven was a sly fellow, and at times he was not lacking in treachery and deceit. But Sea-gull did not suspect him, and the two lived always on very friendly terms. In these far-back times in the north country all the world was dark and there was no light but that of the stars. Sea-gull owned all the daylight, but he was very stingy and he kept it always locked up in a box. He would give none of it to anyone else, and he never let it out of the box except when he needed a little of it to help himself when he went far away on his journeys.

After a time Raven grew envious of Sea-gull's possession. And he said, "It is not fair that Sea-gull should keep the daylight all to himself locked up in a box. It was meant for all the world and not for him alone, and it would be of great value to all of us if he would sometimes let a little of it out." So he went to Sea-gull and said, "Give me some of your daylight. You do not need it all and I can use some of it with advantage."

But Sea-gull said, "No. I want it all for myself. What could you do with daylight, you with your coat as black as night?" and he would not give him any of it. So Raven made up his mind that he would have to get some daylight from Sea-gull by stealth.

Soon afterwards Raven gathered some prickly thorns and burdocks and scattered them on the ground between Sea-gull's house and the beach where the canoes were lying. Then he went to Sea-gull's window and cried loudly, "Our canoes are going adrift in the surf. Come quickly and help me to save them." Sea-gull sprang out of bed and ran half-asleep on his bare feet. But as he ran to the beach the thorns stuck in his bare flesh, and he howled with pain. He crawled back to his house, saying, "My canoe may go adrift if it pleases; I cannot walk because of the splinters in my feet." Raven chuckled to himself, and he moved away, pretending to go to the beach to draw up the canoes. Then he went into Sea-gull's house. Sea-gull was still howling with pain; he was sitting crying on the side of his bed and he was trying to pull the thorns from his feet as best he could. "I will help you," said Raven, "for I have often done this before. I am a very good doctor." So he took an awl made from whale-bone and he caught hold of Sea-gull's foot, with the pretence of removing the thorns. But instead of taking them out he only pushed them in farther until poor Sea-gull howled louder than ever. And Raven said, "It is so dark I cannot see to pull these thorns from your feet. Give me some daylight and I will soon cure you. A doctor must always have a little light." So Sea-gull unlocked the box and lifted the cover just a little bit so that a faint gleam of light came out. "That is better," said Raven. But instead of picking out the thorns he pushed them in as he had done before, until Sea-gull howled and kicked in pain. "Why are you so stingy with your light?" snapped Raven. "Do you think I am an owl and that I can see well enough in the darkness to heal your feet? Open the box wide and I will soon make you well." So saying he purposely fell heavily against Sea-gull and knocked the box on the floor. The cover flew open and daylight escaped and spread quickly over all the world. Poor Sea-gull tried his best to lure it back again into the box, but his efforts proved fruitless, for it had gone for ever. Raven said he was very sorry for the accident, but after he had taken all the thorns from Sea-gull's feet he went home laughing to himself and well pleased because of the success of his trick.

Soon there was light in all the world. But Raven could not see very well, for the light was too bright and his eyes were not accustomed to it. He sat for a time looking towards the east, but he saw there nothing of interest. The next day he saw a bit farther, for he was now getting used to the new conditions. The third day he could see distinctly a line of hills far in the east, rising against the sky, and covered with a blue mist. He looked long at the strange sight. Then he saw far away towards the hill a thin column of smoke lifting heavenwards. He had never seen smoke before, but he had often heard of it from travellers in strange places. "That must be the country of which I have been told," he said. "In that land dwell the people who alone possess Fire. We have searched for it for many ages and now I think we have found it." Then he thought, "We now have the daylight, and what a fine thing it would be if we could also have Fire," and he determined to set out to find it.

On the following day he called his servants together and told them of his plans. He said, "We shall set out at once, for the distance is far." And he asked three of his best servants, Robin, Mole and Flea, to go with him. Flea brought out his little wagon and they all tried to get into it, but it was much too small to hold them. Then they tried Mole's carriage, but it was much too frail, and it had scarcely started to move when it broke down and they all fell out in a heap. Then they tried Robin's carriage, but it was much too high and it toppled over under its heavy load and threw them all to the ground. Then Raven stole Sea-gull's large strong carriage, for Sea-gull was asleep, and it did very well, and they started on their journey, taking turns pushing the carriage along with a pole over the flat plain.

After a strange journey in queer places they reached the land of the people who owned Fire, guided along by the thin column of smoke. The people were not people of earth. Some say they were the Fish people, but that, no man knows. They sat around in a large circle with Fire in their midst, for it was autumn and the days and nights were chill. And Fire was in many places. Raven looked on for a while from afar thinking of the best plan to obtain Fire. Then he said to Robin, "You can move faster than any of us. You must steal Fire. You can fly in quickly, pick it up in your bill and take it back to us and the people will not see nor hear you." So Robin picked out a spot where there were few people, and he darted in quickly and picked up fire in a twinkling and flew back unharmed towards his companions. But he had only taken a very little bit of it. When he got half-way back to his friends, Fire was so hot in his bill that it gave him a strange pain and he had to drop it on the ground. It fell to the earth with a crash and it was so small that it flickered faintly. Robin called to his companions to bring the carriage. Then he stood over Fire and fanned it with his wings to keep it alive. It was very hot, but he stood bravely to his task until his breast was badly scorched and he had to move away. His efforts to save Fire were of no avail, and before his companions reached him Fire had died, and only a black coal remained. And poor Robin's breast was singed, and to this day the breasts of his descendants are a reddish-brown colour because he was scorched while trying to steal Fire ages ago.

Then Raven asked Flea to make the attempt to steal Fire. But Flea said, "I am too little. The heat would roast me to death; and, further, I might miscalculate the distance and hop into the flame." Then Raven asked Mole to try, but Mole said, "Oh no, I am better fitted for other work. My fur would all be singed like Robin's breast." Raven took good care that he would not go himself, for he was a great coward. So he said, "There is a better and easier way. We will steal the baby of the Chief and hold him for ransom. Perhaps they will give us Fire in exchange for him," and they all thought this was a very good idea. Raven asked, "Who will volunteer to steal the baby?" for he always made the others do all the work. Flea said, "I will go. In one jump I will be into the house, and in another jump I will be out again, for I can hop a great distance." But the others laughed and said, "You could not carry the baby; you are too small." The Mole said, "I will go. I can tunnel a passage very quietly under the house and right up to the baby's cradle. I can then steal the baby and no one will hear me or see me." So it was agreed that Mole should go. In a few minutes Mole made his tunnel, and he was soon back with the baby. Then they got into their carriage and hurried home with their prize.

"Then Raven asked the Mole to try, but Mole said, 'Oh no, I am better fitted for other work. My fur would all be singed.'" Illustration by Marcia Lane Foster for Cyrus Macmillan in *Canadian Fairy Tales* (New York: Dodd, Mead and Co., 1922).

When the Chief of the Fire people discovered the loss of his child he was very angry. And in all the land there was great sorrow because the Chief's heir, the hope of the tribe, had gone. And the child's mother and her women wept so bitterly that their tears fell like rain on all the land. The Chief said he would give anything he possessed to find his child. But although his people searched far and near, they could not find the baby. After many days a wayfarer who had come far from the Great Water in the west brought them news that a strange child was living far to the westward in the village by the sea. He said, "He is not of their tribe. He looks like the children of your village," and he advised them to go to see him for themselves. So the Chief sent his men to search for them guided by the wayfarer. When they reached Raven's village they were told that a strange baby was indeed there; the child was described to them, but he was kept out of sight, and Raven would not tell how he had happened to come there. And Raven said, "How do I know he is your Chief's child? People tell strange lies these days. If you want him you can pay for him, for he has caused us much trouble and expense." So the messengers went back and reported to the Chief what they had heard. From the description, the Chief knew that the child was his, so he gave the messengers very valuable presents of pearls and rich robes and sent them back again to ransom his boy. But Raven, when he saw the presents, said, "No, I do not want these gifts; they do not pay me for my trouble," and he would not part with the baby. The messengers again reported to the Chief what had happened. Then the Chief gave them still richer gifts, the best he had in all his land, and sent them back. But again Raven said, "No, your gifts are valueless, compared with my trouble and expense. Say this to your Chief."

When the Chief heard this from his messengers he was sore perplexed, for he had offered the best he had, and he thought that he had reached the end of his resources. So he said, "Go back and ask the people to demand what they wish in exchange for my boy and they will receive it if it can be provided." So the messengers went back to Raven and spoke as they had been commanded. And Raven said, "Only one thing can pay for the child, and that is Fire. Give me Fire and you can take the baby." The messenger laughed and said, "Why did you not say so at first and save us all this trouble and anxiety? Fire is the most plentiful thing in our kingdom, and we hold it in no value." So they returned happy to the Chief. And he sent back much Fire and received his child unharmed from Raven in exchange. And he sent Raven two small stones which the messengers taught Raven how to use. And they said, "If you ever lose Fire or if it dies for lack of food you can always call it back to life with these two little stones." Then they showed him how to make Fire with the two little stones and withered grass, and birch-bark and dry pine, and Raven thought it was very easy. And he felt very proud because he had brought Fire and Light to the earth. He kept Fire for himself for a long time, and although the people clamoured loudly for it, he would not give any of it away. Soon, however, he decided to sell a quantity of it, for he now had the power of making it. So he said to himself, "This is a good way to get many wives," and he announced that he would only sell some of his fire in return for a wife. And many families bought his fire and in exchange he received many wives. And to this day he still has many wives and he still moves about from place to place with a flock of them always around him. But the Indians when they arrived took Fire away from him. Thus Fire came to the Indians in the olden days. And when it has died, as it often does, they still sometimes use Raven's flint stones to bring it back to life.

Illustration by Jessie Willcox Smith for Robert Louis Stevenson, *A Child's Garden of Verses*, Verse 142 (New York: Charles Scribner's Sons, 1905).

Week Four:
IN THE GARDEN

A bird came down the walk:
He did not know I saw;
He bit an angle-worm in halves
And ate the fellow, raw.

And then he drank a dew
From a convenient grass,
And then hopped sidewise to the wall
To let a beetle pass.

He glanced with rapid eyes
That hurried all abroad, —
They looked like frightened beads, I thought;
He stirred his velvet head

Like one in danger; cautious,
I offered him a crumb,
And he unrolled his feathers
And rowed him softer home

Than oars divide the ocean,
Too silver for a seam,
Or butterflies, off banks of noon,
Leap, plashless, as they swim.

EMILY DICKINSON
(1830–1886)

"He placed the arrow on the bow." Illustration by Angel de Cora for Zitkala-Sa in *Old Indian Legends* (Boston, New York, Chicago, London: Ginn & Co., 1901).

Week Five:

WHITE PLUME
Native North American Legend

RETOLD BY MARIE L. McLAUGHLIN

There once lived a young couple who were very happy. The young man was noted throughout the whole nation for his accuracy with the bow and arrow, and was given the title of "Dead Shot," or "He who never misses his mark," and the young woman, noted for her beauty, was named Beautiful Dove.

One day a stork paid this happy couple a visit and left them a fine big boy. The boy cried "Ina, ina" (mother, mother). "Listen to our son," said the mother, "he can speak, and hasn't he a sweet voice?" "Yes," said the father, "it will not be long before he will be able to walk." He set to work making some arrows, and a fine hickory bow for his son. One of the arrows he painted red, one blue, and another yellow. The rest he left the natural color of the wood. When he had completed them, the mother placed them in a fine quiver, all worked in porcupine quills, and hung them up over where the boy slept in his fine hammock of painted moose hide.

At times when the mother would be nursing her son, she would look up at the bow and arrows and talk to her baby, saying: "My son, hurry up and grow fast so you can use your bow and arrows. You will grow up to be as fine a marksman as your father." The baby would coo and stretch his little arms up towards the bright colored quiver as though he understood every word his mother had uttered. Time passed and the boy grew up to a good size, when one day his father said: "Wife, give our son the bow and arrows so that he may learn how to use them." The father taught his son how to string and unstring the bow, and also how to attach the arrow to the string. The red, blue and yellow arrows, he told the boy, were to be used only whenever there was any extra good shooting to be done, so the boy never used these three until he became a master of the art. Then he would practice on eagles and hawks, and never an eagle or hawk continued his flight when the boy shot one of the arrows after him.

One day the boy came running into the tent, exclaiming: "Mother, mother, I have shot and killed the most beautiful bird I ever saw." "Bring it in, my son, and let me look at it." He brought the bird and upon examining it she pronounced it a different type of bird from any she had ever seen. Its feathers were of variegated colors and on its head was a topknot of pure white feathers. The father, returning, asked the boy with which arrow he had killed the bird. "With the red one," answered the boy. "I was so anxious to secure the pretty bird that, although I know I could have killed it with one of my common arrows, I wanted to be certain, so I used the red one." "That is right, my son," said the father. "When you have the least doubt of your aim, always use one of the painted arrows, and you will never miss your mark."

The parents decided to give a big feast in honor of their son killing the strange, beautiful bird. So a great many elderly women were called to the tent of Pretty Dove to assist her in making ready for the big feast. For ten days these women cooked and pounded beef and cherries, and got ready the choicest dishes known to the Indians. Of buffalo, beaver, deer, antelope, moose, bear, quail, grouse, duck of all kinds, geese and plover meats there was an abundance. Fish of all kinds, and every kind of wild fruit were cooked, and when all was in readiness, the heralds went through the different villages, crying out: "Ho-po, ho-po" (now all, now all), "Dead Shot and his wife, Beautiful Dove, invite all of you, young and old, to their tepee to partake of a great feast, given by them in honor of a great bird which their son has killed, and also to select for their son some good name which he will bear through life. So all bring your cups and wooden dishes along with your horn spoons, as there will be plenty to eat. Come, all you council men and chiefs, as they have also a great tent erected for you in which you hold your council."

Thus crying, the heralds made the circle of the village. The guests soon arrived. In front of the tent was a pole stuck in the ground and painted red, and at the top of the pole was fastened the bird of variegated colors; its wings stretched out to their full length and the beautiful white waving so beautifully from its topknot, it was the center of attraction. Half way up the pole was tied the bow and arrow of the young marksman. Long streamers of fine bead and porcupine work waved from the pole and presented a very striking appearance. The bird was faced towards the setting sun. The great chief and medicine men pronounced the bird "Wakan" (something holy).

When the people had finished eating they all fell in line and marched in single file beneath the bird, in order to get a close view of it. By the time this vast crowd had fully viewed the wonderful bird, the sun was just setting clear in the west, when directly over the rays of the sun appeared a cloud in the shape of a bird of variegated colors. The councilmen were called out to look at the cloud, and the head medicine man said that it was a sign that the boy would grow up to be a great chief and hunter, and would have a great many friends and followers.

This ended the feast, but before dispersing, the chief and councilmen bestowed upon the boy the title of White Plume.

One day a stranger came to the village, who was very thin and nearly starved. So weak was he that he could not speak, but made signs for something to eat. Luckily the stranger came to Dead Shot's tent, and as there was always a plentiful supply in his lodge, the stranger soon had a good meal served him. After he had eaten and rested he told his story.

"I came from a very great distance," said he. "The nations where I came from are in a starving condition. No place can they find any buffalo, deer nor antelope. A witch or evil spirit in the shape of a white buffalo has driven all the large game out of the country. Every day this white buffalo comes circling the village, and any one caught outside of their tent is carried away on its horns. In vain have the best marksmen of the tribe tried to shoot it. Their arrows fly wide off the mark, and they have given up trying to kill it as it bears a charmed life. Another evil spirit in the form of a red eagle has driven all the birds of the air out of our country. Every day this eagle circles above the village, and so powerful is it that anyone being caught outside of his tent is descended upon and his skull split open to the brain by the sharp breastbone of the Eagle. Many a marksman has tried his skill on this bird, all to no purpose.

"Another evil spirit in the form of a white rabbit has driven out all the animals which inhabit the ground, and destroyed the fields of corn and turnips, so the nation is starving, as the arrows of the marksmen have also failed to touch the white rabbit. Any one who can kill these three witches will receive as his reward, the choice of two of the most beautiful maidens of our nation. The younger one is the handsomer of the two and has also the sweetest disposition. Many young, and even old men, hearing of this (our chief's) offer, have traveled many miles to try their arrows on the witches, but all to no purpose. Our chief, hearing of your great marksmanship, sent me to try and secure your services to have you come and rid us of these three witches."

Thus spoke the stranger to the hunter. The hunter gazed long and thoughtfully into the dying embers of the camp fire. Then slowly his eyes raised and looked lovingly on his wife who sat opposite to him. Gazing on her beautiful features for a full minute he slowly dropped his gaze back to the dying embers and thus answered his visitor:

"My friend, I feel very much honored by your chief having sent such a great distance for me, and also for the kind offer of his lovely daughter in marriage, if I should succeed, but I must reject the great offer, as I can spare none of my affections to any other woman than to my queen whom you see sitting there."

White Plume had been listening to the conversation and when his father had finished speaking, said: "Father, I am a child no more. I have arrived at manhood. I am not so good a marksman as you, but I will go to this suffering tribe and try to rid them of their three enemies. If this man will rest for a few days and return to his village and inform them of my coming, I will travel along slowly on his trail and arrive at the village a day or two after he reaches there."

"Very well, my son," said the father, "I am sure you will succeed, as you fear nothing, and as to your marksmanship, it is far superior to mine, as your sight is much clearer and aim quicker than mine."

The man rested a few days and one morning started off, after having instructed White Plume as to the trail. White Plume got together what he would need on the trip and was ready for an early start the next morning. That night Dead Shot and his wife sat up away into the night instructing their son how to travel and warning him as to the different kinds of people he must avoid in order to keep out of trouble. "Above all," said the father, "keep a good look out for Unktomi (spider); he is the most tricky of all, and will get you into trouble if you associate with him."

White Plume left early, his father accompanying him for several miles. On parting, the father's last words were: "Look out for Unktomi, my son, he is deceitful and treacherous." "I'll look out for him, father;" so saying he disappeared over a hill. On the way he tried his skill on several hawks and eagles and he did not need to use his painted arrows to kill them, but so skillful was he with the bow and arrows that he could bring down anything that flew with his common arrows. He was drawing near to the end of his destination when he had a large tract of timber to pass through. When he had nearly gotten through the timber he saw an old man sitting on a log, looking wistfully up into a big tree, where sat a number of prairie chickens.

"Hello, grandfather, why are you sitting there looking so downhearted?" asked White Plume. "I am nearly starved, and was just wishing some one would shoot one of those chickens for me, so I could make a good meal on it," said the old man. "I will shoot one for you," said the young man. He strung his bow, placed an arrow on the string, simply seemed to raise the arrow in the direction of the chicken (taking no aim). Twang went out the bow, zip went the arrow and a chicken fell off the limb, only to get caught on another in its descent. "There is your chicken, grandfather." "Oh, my grandson, I am too weak to climb up and get it. Can't you climb up and get it for me?" The young man, pitying the old fellow, proceeded to climb the tree, when the old man stopped him, saying: "Grandson, you have on such fine clothes, it is a pity to spoil them; you had better take them off so as not to spoil the fine porcupine work on them." The young man took off his fine clothes and climbed up into the tree, and securing the chicken, threw it down to the old man. As the young man was scaling down the tree, the old man said: "Iyashkapa, iyashkapa," (stick fast, stick fast). Hearing him say something, he asked, "What did you say, old man?" He answered, "I was only talking to myself." The young man proceeded to descend, but he could not move. His body was stuck fast to the bark of the tree. In vain did he beg the old man to release him. The old Unktomi, for he it was, only laughed and said: "I will go now and kill the evil spirits, I have your wonderful bow and arrows and I cannot miss them. I will marry the chief's daughter, and you can stay up in that tree and die there."

So saying, he put on White Plume's fine clothes, took his bow and arrows and went to the village. As White Plume was expected at any minute, the whole village was watching for him, and when Unktomi came into sight the young men ran to him with a painted robe, sat him down on it and slowly raising him up they carried him to the tent of the chief. So certain were they that he would kill the evil spirits that the chief told him to choose one of the daughters at once for his wife. (Before the arrival of White Plume, hearing of him being so handsome, the two girls had quarreled over which should marry him, but upon seeing him the younger was not anxious to become his wife.) So Unktomi chose the older one of the sisters, and was given a large tent in which to live. The younger sister went to her mother's tent to live, and the older was very proud, as she was married to the man who would save the nation from starvation. The next morning there was a great commotion in camp, and there came the cry that the white buffalo was coming. "Get ready, son-in-law, and kill the buffalo," said the chief.

Unktomi took the bow and arrows and shot as the buffalo passed, but the arrow went wide off its mark. Next came the eagle, and again he shot and missed. Then came the rabbit, and again he missed.

"Wait until tomorrow, I will kill them all. My blanket caught in my bow and spoiled my aim." The people were very much disappointed, and the chief, suspecting that all was not right, sent for the young man who had visited Dead Shot's tepee. When the young man arrived, the chief asked: "Did you see White Plume when you went to Dead Shot's camp?" "Yes, I did, and ate with him many times. I stayed at his father's tepee all the time I was there," said the young man. "Would you recognize him if you saw him again?" asked the chief. "Any one who had but one glimpse of White Plume would surely recognize him when he saw him again, as he is the most handsome man I ever saw," said the young man.

"Come with me to the tent of my son-in-law and take a good look at him, but don't say what you think until we come away." The two went to the tent of Unktomi, and when the young man saw him he knew it was not White Plume, although it was White Plume's bow and arrows that hung at the head of the bed, and he also recognized the clothes as belonging to White Plume. When they had returned to the chief's tent, the young man told what he knew and what he thought. "I think this is some Unktomi who has played some trick on White Plume and has taken his bow and arrows and also his clothes, and hearing of your offer, is here impersonating White Plume. Had White Plume drawn the bow on the buffalo, eagle and rabbit today, we would have been rid of them, so I think we had better scare this Unktomi into telling us where White Plume is," said the young man.

"Wait until he tries to kill the witches again tomorrow," said the chief.

In the meantime the younger daughter had taken an axe and gone into the woods in search of dry wood. She went quite a little distance into the wood and was chopping a dry log. Stopping to rest a little she heard some one saying: "Whoever you are, come over here and chop this tree down so that I may get loose." Going to where the big tree stood, she saw a man stuck onto the side of the tree. "If I chop it down the fall will kill you," said the girl. "No, chop it on the opposite side from me, and the tree will fall that way. If the fall kills me, it will be better than hanging up here and starving to death," said White Plume, for it was he.

The girl chopped the tree down and when she saw that it had not killed the man, she said: "What shall I do now?" "Loosen the bark from the tree and then get some stones and heat them. Get some water and sage and put your blanket over me." She did as told and when the steam arose from the water being poured upon the heated rocks, the bark loosened from his body and he arose. When he stood up, she saw how handsome he was. "You have saved my life," said he. "Will you be my wife?" "I will," said she. He then told her how the old man had fooled him into this trap and took his bow and arrows, also his fine porcupine worked clothes, and had gone off, leaving him to die. She, in turn, told him all that had happened in camp since a man, calling himself White Plume, came there and married her sister before he shot at the witches, and when he came to shoot at them, missed every shot. "Let us make haste, as the bad Unktomi may ruin my arrows." They approached the camp and whilst White Plume waited outside, his promised wife entered Unktomi's tent and said: "Unktomi, White Plume is standing outside and he wants his clothes and bow and arrows." "Oh, yes, I borrowed them and forgot to return them; make haste and give them to him."

Upon receiving his clothes, he was very much provoked to find his fine clothes wrinkled and his bow twisted, while the arrows were twisted out of shape. He laid the clothes down, also the bows and arrows, and passing his hand over them, they assumed their right shapes again. The daughter took White Plume to her father's tent and upon hearing the story he at once sent for his warriors and had them form a circle around Unktomi's tent, and if he attempted to escape to catch him and tie him to a tree, as he (the chief) had determined to settle accounts with him for his treatment of White Plume, and the deception employed in winning the chief's eldest daughter. About midnight the guard noticed something crawling along close to the ground, and seizing him found it was Unktomi trying to make his escape before daylight, whereupon they tied him to a tree. "Why do you treat me thus," cried Unktomi, "I was just going out in search of medicine to rub on my arrows, so I can kill the witches." "You will need medicine to rub on yourself when the chief gets through with you," said the young man who had discovered that Unktomi was impersonating White Plume.

In the morning the herald announced that the real White Plume had arrived, and the chief desired the whole nation to witness his marksmanship. Then came the cry: "The White Buffalo comes." Taking his red arrow, White Plume stood ready. When the buffalo got about opposite him, he let his arrow fly. The buffalo bounded high in the air and came down with all four feet drawn together under its body, the red arrow having passed clear through the animal, piercing the buffalo's heart. A loud cheer went up from the village.

"You shall use the hide for your bed," said the chief to White Plume. Next came a cry, "the eagle, the eagle." From the north came an enormous red eagle. So strong was he, that as he soared through the air his wings made a humming sound as the rumble of distant thunder. On he came, and just as he circled the tent of the chief, White Plume bent his bow, with all his strength drew the arrow back to the flint point, and sent the blue arrow on its mission of death. So swiftly had the arrow passed through the eagle's body that, thinking White Plume had missed, a great wail went up from the crowd, but when they saw the eagle stop in his flight, give a few flaps of his wings, and then fall with a heavy thud into the center of the village, there was a greater cheer than before. "The red eagle shall be used to decorate the seat of honor in your tepee," said the chief to White Plume. Last came the white rabbit. "Aim good, aim good, son-in-law," said the chief. "If you kill him you will have his skin for a rug." Along came the white rabbit, and White Plume sent his arrow in search of rabbit's heart, which it found, and stopped Mr. Rabbit's tricks forever.

The chief then called all of the people together and before them all took a hundred willows and broke them one at a time over Unktomi's back. Then he turned him loose. Unktomi, being so ashamed, ran off into the woods and hid in the deepest and darkest corner he could find. This is why Unktomis (spiders) are always found in dark corners, and anyone who is deceitful or untruthful is called a descendant of the Unktomi tribe.

Week Five:
THE CHILD OF THE
EVENING STAR
Native North American Legend

RETOLD BY WILLIAM TROWBRIDGE LARNED

Once upon a time, on the shores of the great lake, Gitchee Gumee, there lived a hunter who had ten beautiful young daughters. Their hair was dark and glossy as the wings of the blackbird, and when they walked or ran it was with the grace and freedom of the deer in the forest.

Thus it was that many suitors came to court them—brave and handsome young men, straight as arrows, fleet of foot, who could travel from sun to sun without fatigue. They were sons of the prairie, wonderful horsemen who would ride at breakneck speed without saddle or stirrup. They could catch a wild horse with a noose, tame him in a magical way by breathing into his nostrils, then mount him and gallop off as if he always had been ridden. There were those also who came from afar in canoes, across the waters of the Great Lake, canoes which shot swiftly along, urged by the strong, silent sweep of the paddle.

All of them brought presents with which they hoped to gain the father's favor. Feathers from the wings of the eagle who soars high up near the sun; furs of fox and beaver and the thick, curly hair of the bison; beads of many colors, and wampum, the shells which the Indians used for money; the quills of the porcupine and the claws of the grizzly bear; deerskin dressed to such a softness that it crumpled up in the hands— these and many other things they brought.

One by one, the daughters were wooed and married, until nine of them had chosen husbands. One by one, other tents were reared, so that instead of the single family lodge on the shores of the lake there were tents enough to form a little village. For the country was a rich one, and there was game and fish enough for all.

There remained the youngest daughter, Oweenee—the fairest of them all. Gentle as she was beautiful, none was so kind of heart. Unlike her proud and talkative elder sisters, Oweenee was shy and modest, and spoke but little. She loved to wander alone in the woods, with no company but the birds and squirrels and her own thoughts. What these thoughts were we can only guess; from her dreamy eyes and sweet expression, one could but suppose that nothing selfish or mean or hateful ever came into her mind. Yet Oweenee, modest though she was, had a spirit of her own. More than one suitor had found this out. More than one conceited young man, confident that he could win her, went away crestfallen when Oweenee began to laugh at him.

The truth is, Oweenee seemed hard to please. Suitor after suitor came—handsome, tall young men, the handsomest and the bravest in all the country round. Yet this fawn-eyed maiden would have none of them. One was too tall, another too short; one too thin, another too fat. At least, that was the excuse she gave for sending them away. Her proud sisters had little patience with her. It seemed to be questioning their own taste; for Oweenee, had she said the word, might have gained a husband more attractive than any of theirs. Yet no one was good enough. They could not understand her; so they ended by despising her as a silly and unreasonable girl.

Her father, too, who loved her dearly and wished her to be happy, was much puzzled. "Tell me, my daughter," he said to her one day, "Is it your wish never to marry? The handsomest young men in the land have sought you in marriage, and you have sent them all away—often with a poor excuse. Why is it?"

Oweenee looked at him with her large, dark eyes.

"She loved to wander alone in the woods." Illustration by John Rae for William Trowbridge Larned in *Indians of North America* (Joliet, IL, New York, and Boston: P. F. Volland, 1923).

"Father," she said at last. "It is not that I am wilful. But it seems somehow as if I had the power to look into the hearts of men. It is the heart of a man, and not his face, that really matters; and I have not yet found one youth who in this sense is really beautiful."

Soon after, a strange thing happened. There came into the little village an Indian named Osseo, many years older than Oweenee. He was poor and ugly, too. Yet Oweenee married him.

How the tongues of her nine proud sisters did wag! Had the spoiled little thing lost her mind? they asked. Oh, well! They always knew she would come to a bad end; but it was pretty hard on the family.

Of course they could not know what Oweenee had seen at once— that Osseo had a generous nature and a heart of gold; that beneath his outward ugliness was the beauty of a noble mind, and the fire and passion of a poet. That is why Oweenee loved him; knowing, too, that he needed her care, she loved him all the more.

Now, though Oweenee did not suspect it, Osseo was really a beautiful youth on whom an evil spell had been cast. He was in truth the son of the King of the Evening Star—that Evening Star which shines so gloriously in the western sky, just above the rim of the earth, as the sun is setting. Often on a clear evening it hung suspended in the purple twilight like some glittering jewel. So close it seemed, and so friendly, that the little children would reach out their hands, thinking that they might grasp it ere it was swallowed by the night, and keep it always for their own. But the older ones would say: "Surely it must be a bead on the garments of the Great Spirit as he walks in the evening through the garden of the heavens."

Little did they know that the poor, despised Osseo had really descended from that star. And when he, too, stretched out his arms toward it, and murmured words they could not understand, they all made sport of him.

There came a time when a great feast was prepared in a neighboring village, and all of Oweenee's kinsfolk were invited to attend. They set out on foot—the nine proud sisters, with their husbands, walking ahead, much pleased with themselves and their finery, and all chattering like magpies. But Oweenee walked behind in silence, and with her walked Osseo.

The sun had set; in the purple twilight, over the edge of the earth, sparkled the Evening Star. Osseo, pausing, stretched out his hands toward it, as if imploring pity; but when the others saw him in this attitude they all made merry, laughing and joking and making unkind remarks.

"Instead of looking up in the sky," said one of the sisters, "he had better be looking on the ground. Else he may stumble and break his neck." Then calling back to him, she cried: "Look out! Here's a big log. Do you think you can manage to climb over it?"

Osseo made no answer; but when he came to the log he paused again. It was the trunk of a huge oak-tree blown down by the wind. There it had lain for years, just as it fell; and the leaves of many summers lay thick upon it. There was one thing, though, the sisters had not noticed. The tree-trunk was not a solid one, but hollow, and so big around that a man could walk inside it from one end to the other without stooping.

But Osseo did not pause because he was unable to climb over it. There was something mysterious and magical in the appearance of the great hollow trunk; and he gazed at it a long time, as if he had seen it in a dream, and had been looking for it ever since.

"What is it, Osseo?" asked Oweenee, touching him on the arm. "Do you see something that I cannot see?"

But Osseo only gave a shout that echoed through the forest, and leaped inside the log. Then as Oweenee, a little alarmed, stood there waiting, the figure of a man came out from the other end. Could this be Osseo? Yes, it was he— but how transformed! No longer bent and ugly, no longer weak and ailing; but a beautiful youth—vigorous and straight and tall. His enchantment was at an end.

But the evil spell had not been wholly lifted, after all. As Osseo approached he saw that a great change was taking place in his loved one. Her glossy black hair was turning white, deep wrinkles lined her face; she walked with a feeble step, leaning on a staff. Though he had regained his youth and beauty, she in turn had suddenly grown old.

"O, my dearest one!" he cried. "The Evening Star has mocked me in letting this misfortune come upon you. Better far had I remained as I was; gladly would I have borne the insults and laughter of your people rather than you should be made to suffer."

"As long as you love me," answered Oweenee, "I am perfectly content. If I had the choice to make, and only one of us could be young and fair, it is you that I would wish to be beautiful."

Then he took her in his arms and caressed her, vowing that he loved her more than ever for her goodness of heart; and together they walked hand in hand, as lovers do.

When the proud sisters saw what had happened they could scarcely believe their eyes. They looked enviously at Osseo, who was now far handsomer than any one of their husbands, and much their superior in every other way. In his eyes was the wonderful light of the Evening Star, and when he spoke all men turned to listen and admire him. But the hard-hearted sisters had no pity for Oweenee. Indeed, it rather pleased them to see that she could no longer dim their beauty, and to realize that people would no longer be singing her praises in their jealous ears.

The feast was spread, and all made merry but Osseo. He sat like one in a dream, neither eating nor drinking. From time to time he would press Oweenee's hand, and speak a word of comfort in her ear. But for the most part he sat there, gazing through the door of the tent at the star-besprinkled sky.

Soon a silence fell on all the company. From out of the night, from the dark, mysterious forest, came the sound of music—a low, sweet music that was like, yet unlike, the song sung by the thrush in summer twilight. It was magical music such as none had ever heard, coming, as it seemed, from a great distance, and rising and falling on the quiet summer evening. All those at the feast wondered as they listened. And well they might! For what to them was only music, was to Osseo a voice that he understood, a voice from the sky itself, the voice of the Evening Star. These were the words that he heard:

"Suffer no more, my son; for the evil spell is broken, and hereafter no magician shall work you harm. Suffer no more; for the time has come when you shall leave the earth and dwell here with me in the heavens. Before you is a dish on which my light has fallen, blessing it and giving it a magic virtue. Eat of this dish, Osseo, and all will be well."

So Osseo tasted the food before him, and behold! The tent began to tremble, and rose slowly into the air; up, up above the tree-tops—up, up toward the stars. As it rose, the things within it were wondrously changed. The kettles of clay became bowls of silver, the wooden dishes were scarlet shells, while the bark of the roof and the poles supporting it were transformed into some glittering substance that sparkled in the rays of the stars. Higher and higher it rose. Then the nine proud sisters and their husbands were all changed into birds. The men became robins, thrushes and woodpeckers. The sisters were changed into various birds with bright plumage; the four who had chattered most, whose tongues were always wagging, now appeared in the feathers of the magpie and bluejay.

Osseo sat gazing at Oweenee. Would she, too, change into a bird, and be lost to him? The very thought of it made him bow his head with grief; then, as he looked at her once more, he saw her beauty suddenly restored, while the color of her garments was the color only to be found where the dyes of the rainbow are made.

Again the tent swayed and trembled as the currents of the air bore it higher and higher, into and above the clouds; up, up, up—till at last it settled gently on the land of the Evening Star.

Osseo and Oweenee caught all the birds, and put them in a great silver cage, where they seemed quite content in each other's company. Scarcely was this done when Osseo's father, the King of the Evening Star, came to greet them. He was attired in a flowing robe, spun from star-dust, and his long white hair hung like a cloud upon his shoulders.

"Welcome," he said, "my dear children. Welcome to the kingdom in the sky that has always awaited you. The trials you have passed through have been bitter; but you have borne them bravely, and now you will be rewarded for all your courage and devotion. Here you will live happily; yet of one thing you must beware."

He pointed to a little star in the distance—a little, winking star, hidden from time to time by a cloud of vapor.

"On that star," he continued, "lives a magician named Wabeno. He has the power to dart his rays, like so many arrows, at those he wishes to injure. He has always been my enemy; it was he who changed Osseo into an old man and cast him down upon the earth. Have a care that his light does not fall upon you. Luckily, his power for evil has been greatly weakened; for the friendly clouds have come to my assistance, and form a screen of vapor through which his arrows cannot penetrate."

The happy pair fell upon their knees, and kissed his hands in gratitude.

"But these birds," said Osseo, rising and pointing to the cage. "Is this also the work of Wabeno, the magician?"

"No," answered the King of the Evening Star. "It was my own power, the power of love, that caused your tent to rise and bear you hither. It was likewise by my power that the envious sisters and their husbands were transformed into birds. Because they hated you and mocked you, and were cruel and scornful to the weak and the old, I have done this thing. It is not so great a punishment as they deserve. Here in the silver cage they will be happy enough, proud of their handsome plumage, strutting and twittering to their hearts' content. Hang the cage there, at the doorway of my dwelling. They shall be well cared for."

Thus it was that Osseo and Oweenee came to live in the kingdom of the Evening Star; and, as the years passed by, the little winking star where Wabeno, the magician, lived grew pale and paler and dim and dimmer, till it quite lost its power to harm. Meanwhile a little son had come to make their happiness more perfect, a charming boy with the dark, dreamy eyes of his mother and the strength and courage of Osseo.

It was a wonderful place for a little boy to live in—close to the stars and the moon, with the sky so near that it seemed a kind of curtain for his bed, and all the glory of the heavens spread out before him. But sometimes he was lonely, and wondered what the Earth was like—the Earth his father and mother had come from. He could see it far, far below—so far that it looked no bigger than an orange; and sometimes he would stretch out his hands toward it, just as the little children on earth stretch out their hands for the moon.

His father had made him a bow, with little arrows, and this was a great delight to him. But still he was lonely, and wondered what the little boys and girls on earth were doing, and whether they would be nice to play with. The Earth must be a pretty place, he thought, with so many people living on it. His mother had told him strange stories of that far-away land, with its lovely lakes and rivers, its great, green forests where the deer and the squirrel lived, and the yellow, rolling prairies swarming with buffalo.

These birds, too, in the great silver cage had come from the Earth, he was told; and there were thousands and thousands just like them, as well as others even more beautiful that he had never seen at all. Swans with long, curved necks, that floated gracefully on the waters; whip-poor-wills that called at night from the woods; the robin redbreast, the dove and the swallow. What wonderful birds they must be!

Sometimes he would sit near the cage, trying to understand the language of the feathered creatures inside. One day a strange idea came into his head. He would open the door of the cage and let them out. Then they would fly back to Earth, and perhaps they would take him with them. When his father and mother missed him they would be sure to follow him to the Earth, and then—

He could not quite see just how it would all end. But he found himself quite close to the cage, and the first thing he knew he had opened the door and let out all the birds. Round and round they flew; and now he was half sorry, and a little afraid as well. If the birds flew back to Earth, and left him there, what would his grandfather say?

"Come back, come back!" he called.

But the birds only flew around him in circles, and paid no attention to him. At any moment they might be winging their way to the

Earth. "Come back, I tell you!" he cried, stamping his foot and waving his little bow. "Come back, I say, or I'll shoot you."

Then, as they would not obey him, he fitted an arrow to his bow and let it fly. So well did he aim that the arrow sped through the plumage of a bird, and the feathers fell all around. The bird itself, a little stunned but not much hurt, fell down; and a tiny trickle of blood stained the ground where it lay. But it was no longer a bird, with an arrow in its wing; instead, there stood in its place a beautiful young woman.

Now, no one who lives in the stars is ever permitted to shed blood, whether it be of man, beast or bird. So when the few drops fell upon the Evening Star, everything was changed. The boy suddenly found himself sinking slowly downward, held up by invisible hands, yet ever sinking closer and closer to the Earth. Soon he could see its green hills and the swans floating on the water, till at last he rested on a grassy island in a great lake. Lying there, and looking up at the sky, he could see the tent descending, too. Down it softly drifted, till it in turn sank upon the island; and in it were his father and mother, Osseo and Oweenee—returned to earth, to live once more among men and women and teach them how to live. For they had learned many things in their life upon the Evening Star; and the children of Earth would be better for the knowledge.

As they stood there, hand in hand, all the enchanted birds came fluttering after, falling and fluttering through the air. Then as each one touched the Earth, it was no longer a bird they saw, but a human being. A human being, yet not quite as before; for now they were only dwarfs, Little People, or Pygmies; Puk-Wudjies, as the Indians called them. Happy Little People they became, seen only by a few. Fishermen, they say, would sometimes get a glimpse of them—dancing in the light of the Evening Star, of a summer night, on the sandy, level beach of the Great Lake.

Before his tail was grown the timid Robin had become as brave as any of the children, for, you know, after you begin to be brave you always want to go on. But the Garter Snake says that Mrs. Robin is the bravest of the family.

"'A long basket, with something white inside; and it's crying!'" Illustration by Etheldred B. Barry for Laura Elizabeth Howe Richards in *The Green Satin Gown* (Boston: Dana Estes and Company, 1903).

Week Eight:

Little Benjamin

American Short Story

by Laura E. Richards

think the kitty wants to come in," said Mother Golden. "I hear him crying somewhere. Won't you go and let him in, Adam?"

Adam laid down his book and went out; the whole family looked up cheerfully, expecting to see Aladdin, the great Maltese cat, enter with his stately port. There was a pause; then Adam came back with a white, scared face, and looked at his father without speaking.

"What is the matter, my son?" asked Father Golden.

"Is Kitty hurt?" asked Mother Golden, anxiously.

"Was it that dog of Jackson's?" cried Lemuel, Mary, Ruth, and Joseph.

"The cat isn't there!" said Adam. "It's—it's a basket, father."

"A basket? What does the boy mean?"

"A long basket, with something white inside; and it's crying!"

The boy had left the door open, and at this moment a sound came through it, a long, low, plaintive cry.

"My heart!" said Mother Golden; and she was out of the door in a flash.

"See there now!" said Father Golden, reprovingly. "Your mother's smarter than any of you to-day. Go and help her, some of you!"

The children tumbled headlong toward the door, but were met by Mother Golden returning, bearing in her strong arms a long basket, in which was indeed something white and fluffy that cried.

"A baby!" exclaimed Father Golden.

"A baby!" echoed Mary, Lemuel, Ruth, and Joseph.

"Well, I knew it was a baby," protested Adam; "but I didn't like to say so."

Mother Golden lifted the child out and held it in a certain way; the cries ceased, and the little creature nestled close against her and looked up in her face.

"My heart!" said Mother Golden again. "Come here, girls!"

The girls pressed forward eagerly; the boys hung back, and glanced at their father; these were women's matters.

"It's got hair!" cried Ruth, in rapture. "Mother! real hair, and it curls; see it curl!"

"Look at its little hands!" murmured Mary. "They're like pink shells, only soft. Oh! see it move them, Ruth!" She caught her sister's arm in a sudden movement of delight.

"Oh, mother, mayn't we keep it?" cried both girls at once.

Mother Golden was examining the baby's clothes.

"Cambric slip, fine enough, but not so terrible fine. Flannel blanket, machine-embroidered—stop! here's a note."

She opened a folded paper, and read a few words, written in a carefully rough hand.

"His mother is dead, his father a waif. Ask the woman with the kind eyes to take care of him, for Christ's sake."

"My heart!" said Mother Golden, again.

"It's a boy, then!" said Father Golden, brightening perceptibly. He came forward, the boys edging forward too, encouraged by another masculine presence.

"It's a boy, and a beauty!" said Mother Golden, wiping her eyes. "I never see a prettier child. Poor mother, to have to go and leave him. Father, what do you say?"

"It's for you to say, mother;" said Father Golden. "It's to you the child was sent."

"Do you suppose 'twas me that was meant? They might have mistaken the house."

"Don't talk foolishness!" said Father Golden. "The question is, what shall we do with it? There's places, a plenty, where foundlings have the best of bringing up; and you've got care enough, as it is, mother, without taking on any more."

"Oh! we could help!" cried Mary. "I could wash and dress it, I know I could, and I'd just love to."

"So could I!" said twelve-year-old Ruth. "We'd take turns, Mary and I. Do let's keep it, mother!"

"It's a great responsibility! "said Father Golden.

"Great Jemima!" said Mother Golden, with a sniff. "If I couldn't take the responsibility of a baby, I'd give up."

Father Golden's mind moved slowly, and while he was meditating a reply, his wife issued various commands, and went through some intricate feminine manoeuvres, with the effect of increased fluffiness on the baby's part. In five minutes she was feeding the child with warm milk from a spoon, and proclaiming that he ate "like a Major!"

The boys, gaining more and more confidence, were now close at her knee, and watched the process with eager eyes.

"He's swallering like anything!" cried Lemuel. "I can see him do it with his throat, same as anybody."

"See him grab the spoon!" said Joseph. "My! ain't he strong? Can he talk, mother?"

"Joe, you chuckle-head!" said Adam, who was sixteen, and knew most things. "How can he talk, when he hasn't got any teeth?"

"Uncle Rastus hasn't got any teeth," retorted Joseph, "and he talks like a buzz-saw."

"Hush, Joseph!" said Mother Golden, reprovingly. "Your Uncle Rastus is a man of years."

"Yes, mother!" said Joseph, meekly.

"Baby *has* got a tooth, too, Adam!" Mother Golden continued, triumphantly. "I feel it pricking through the gum this minute. And he so good, and laughing like a sunflower! Did it hurt him, then, a little precious man? he shall have a nice ring to-morrow day, to bitey on, so he shall!"

"I suppose, then, he must be as much as a week old," hazarded Adam, in an off-hand tone. "They are never born with teeth, are they, unless they are going to be Richard the Thirds, or something wonderful?"

"Perhaps he is!" said Ruth. "He looks wonderful enough for Richard the Twentieth, or anything."

But—"A week old!" said Mother Golden. "It's time there was a baby in this house, if you don't know better than that, Adam. About six months old I call him, and as pretty a child as ever I saw, even my own."

She looked half-defiantly at Father Golden, who returned the look with one of mild deprecation.

"I was only thinking of the care 'twould be to you, mother," he said. "We're bound to make inquiries, and report the case, and so forth; but if nothing comes of that, we might keep the child for a spell, and see how things turn out."

"That's what I was thinking!" said Mother Golden, eagerly. "I was thinking anyway, Joel, 'twould be best to keep him through his teething and stomach troubles, and give him a good start in the way of proper food and nursing. At them homes and nurseries, they mean well, but the most of them's young, and they *don't* understand a child's stomach. It's experience they need, not good-will, I'm well aware. Of course, when Baby begun to be a boy, things might be different. You work hard enough as it is, father, and there's places, no doubt, could do better for him, maybe, than what we could. But well, seeing whose name he come in, I *do* feel to see him through his teething."

"Children, what do you say?" asked Father Golden. "You're old enough to have your opinion, even the youngest of you."

"Oh, keep him! keep him!" clamored the three younger children.

Adam and Lemuel exchanged a glance of grave inquiry.

"I guess he d better stay, father!" said Adam.

"I think so, too!" said Lemuel; and both gave something like a sigh of relief.

"Then that's settled," said Father Golden, "saying and supposing that no objection turns up. Next thing is, what shall we call this child ?"

All eyes were fixed on the baby, who, now full of warm milk, sat throned on Mother Golden's knee, blinking content.

It was a pretty picture: the rosy, dimpled creature, the yellow floss ruffled all over his head, his absurd little mouth open in a beaming smile; beaming above him, Mother Golden's placid face in its frame of silver hair; fronting them, Father Golden in his big leather chair, solid, comfortable, benevolent; and the five children, their honest, sober faces lighted up with unusual excitement. A pleasant, homelike picture. Nothing remarkable in the way of setting; the room, with its stuffed chairs, its tidies, and cabinet organ, was only unlike other such rooms from the fact that Mother Golden habitually sat in it; she could keep even haircloth from being commonplace. But now, all the light in the room seemed to centre on the yellow flossy curls against her breast.

"A-goo!" said the baby, in a winning gurgle.

"He says his name's Goo!" announced Joseph.

"Don't be a chuckle-head, Joe!" said Adam. "What was the name on the paper, mother?"

"It said his father is a Waif; but I don't take that to be a Christian name. Surname, more likely, shouldn't you say, father?"

"Not a Christian name, certainly," said Father Golden. "Not much of a name anyhow, 'pears to me. We'd better give the child a suitable name, mother, saying and supposing no objection turns up. Coming into a Christian family, let him have Christian baptism, I say."

"Oh, call him Arthur!"

"Bill!"

"Richard!"

"Charlie!"

"Reginald!" cried the children in chorus.

"I do love a Bible name!" said Mother Golden, pensively. "It gives a child a good start, so to say, and makes him think when he hears himself named, or ought so to do. All our own children has Bible names, father; don't let us cut the little stranger off from his privilege."

"But Bible names are so ugly!" objected Lemuel, who was sensitive, and suffered under his own cognomen.

"Son," said Father Golden, "your mother chooses the names in this family."

"Yes, father!" said Lemuel.

"Lemuel, dear, you was named for a king!" said Mother Golden. "He was a good boy to his mother, and so are you. Bring the Bible, and let us see what it opens at. Joseph, you are the youngest, you shall open it."

Joseph opened the great brown leather Bible, and closing his eyes, laid his hand on the page; then looking down, he read:

"'There is little Benjamin their ruler, and the princes of Judah their council: the princes of Zebulun and the princes of Nephtali.'"

"Zebulun and Nephtali are outlandish-sounding names," said Mother Golden. "I never knew but one Nephtali, and he squinted. Benjamin shall be this child's name. Little Benjamin: the Lord bless and keep him!"

"Amen!" said Father Golden.

PART II

"Father, may I come in, if you are not busy?"

It was Mary who spoke; Mary, the dear eldest daughter, now a woman grown, grave and mild, trying hard to fill the place left empty these two years, since Mother Golden went smiling out of life.

Father Golden looked up from his book; he was an old man now, but his eyes were still young and kind.

"What is it, daughter Mary?"

"The same old story, father dear; Benny in mischief again. This time he has rubbed soot on all the door-handles, and the whole house is black with it. I hate to trouble you, father, but I expect you'll have to speak to him. I do love the child so, I'm not strict enough—I'm ashamed to say it, but they all think so, and I know it's true—and Adam is too strict."

"Yes, Adam is too strict," said Father Golden. He looked at a portrait that stood on his desk, a framed photograph of Mother Golden.

"I'll speak to the child, Mary," he said. I'll see that this does not happen again. What is it, Ruthie?"

"I was looking for Mary, father. I wanted—oh, Mary! what shall I do with Benny? he has tied Rover and the cat together by their tails, and they are rushing all about the garden almost crazy. I must finish this work, so I can't attend to it. He says he is playing Samson. I wish you would speak to him, father."

"I will do so, Ruth, I will do so. Don't be distressed, my daughter."

"But he is so naughty, father! he is so different from the other boys. Joe never used to play such tricks when he was little."

"The spring vacation will be over soon now, Ruth," said Sister Mary. "He is always better when he is at work, and there is so little for a boy to do just at this time of year."

"I left Joe trying to catch the poor creatures," said Ruth. "Here he comes now."

Joe, a tall lad of seventeen, entered with a face of tragedy.

"Any harm done, Joseph?" asked Father Golden, glancing at the portrait on his desk.

"It's that kid again, father!" said Joe. "Poor old Rover—"

"Father knows about that, Joe!" said Mary, gently.

"Did you get them apart?" cried Ruth.

"Yes, I did, but not till they had smashed most of the glass in the kitchen windows, and trampled all over Mary's geraniums. Something has got to be done about that youngster, father. He's getting to be a perfect nuisance."

"I am thinking of doing something about him, son Joseph," said Father Golden. "Are your brothers in the house?"

"I think I heard them come in just now, sir. Do you want to see them?"

Apparently Adam and Lemuel wanted to see their father, for they appeared in the doorway at this moment: quiet-looking men, with grave, "set" faces; the hair already beginning to edge away from their temples.

"You are back early from the office, boys!" said Father Golden.

"We came as soon as we got the message," said Adam. "I hope nothing is wrong, father."

"What message, Adam ?"

"Didn't you send for us? Benny came running in, all out of breath, and said you wished to see us at once. If he has been playing tricks again—"

Adam's grave face darkened into sternness. The trick was too evident.

"Something must be done about that boy, father!" he said. "He is the torment of the whole family."

"No one can live a day in peace!" said Lemuel.

"No dumb creature's life is safe!" said Joe.

"He breaks everything he lays hands on," said Ruth, "and he won't keep his hands off anything."

"You were all little once, boys!" said Mary.

"We never behaved in this kind of way!" said the brothers, sedate from their cradles. "Something must be done!"

"You are right," said Father Golden. "Something must be done."

Glancing once more at the portrait of Mother Golden, he turned and faced his children with grave looks.

"Sit down, sons and daughters!" said the old man. "I have something to say to you."

The young people obeyed, wondering, but not questioning. Father Golden was head of the house.

"You all come to me," said Father Golden, "with complaints of little Benjamin. It is singular that you should come today, for I have been waiting for this day to speak to you about the child myself."

He paused for a moment; then added, weighing his words slowly, as was his wont when much in earnest, "Ten years ago today, that child was left on our door-step."

The brothers and sisters uttered an exclamation, half surprised, half acquiescent.

"It doesn t seem so long!" said Adam.

"It seems longer!" said Mary.

"I keep forgetting he came that way!" murmured Joe.

"I felt doubtful about taking him in," Father Golden went on. "But your mother wished it; you all wished it. We decided to keep him for a spell, and give him a good start in life, and we have kept him till now."

Of course we have kept him!" said Ruth.

"Naturally!" said Lemuel.

Adam and Mary said nothing, but looked earnestly at their father.

"Little Benjamin is now ten years old, more or less," said Father Golden. "You are men and women grown; even Joseph is seventeen. Your mother has entered into the rest that is reserved for the people of God, and I am looking forward in the hope that, not through any merit of mine, but the merciful grace of God, I may soon be called to join her. Adam and Lemuel, you are settled in the business, and looking forward to making homes of your own with worthy young women. Joseph is going to college, which is a new thing in our family, but one I approve, seeing his faculty appears to lie that way. Ruth will make a first-rate dressmaker, I am told by those who know. Mary—"

His quiet voice faltered. Mary took his hand and kissed it passionately; a sob broke from her, and she turned her face away from the brothers and sister who loved but did not understand her. They looked at her with grave compassion, but no one would have thought of interrupting Father Golden.

"Mary, you are the home-maker," the old man went on. "I hope that when I am gone this home will still be here, with you at the head of it. You are your mother's own daughter; there is no more to say."

He was silent for a time, and then continued.

"There remains little Benjamin, a child of ten years. He is no kin to us; an orphan, or as good as one; no person has ever claimed him, or ever will. The time has come to decide what shall be done with the child."

Again he paused, and looked around. The serious young faces were all intent upon him; in some, the intentness seemed deepening into trouble, but no one spoke or moved.

"We have done all that we undertook to do for him, that night we took him in, and more. We have brought him—I should say your mother brought him—through his sickly days; we 'most lost him, you remember, when he was two years old, with the croup and he is now a healthy, hearty child, and will likely make a strong man. He has been well treated, well fed and clothed, maybe better than he would have been by his own parents if so't had been. He is turning out wild and mischievous, though he has a good heart, none better; and you all, except Mary, come to me with complaints of him.

"Now, this thing has gone far enough. One of two things: either this boy is to be sent away to some institution, to take his place among other orphans and foundlings, or he must be one of you for now and always, to share alike with you while I live, to be bore with and helped by each and every one of you as if he was your own blood, and to have his share of the property when I am gone. Sons and daughters, this question is for you to decide. I shall say nothing. My life is 'most over, yours is just beginning. I have no great amount to leave you, but 'twill be comfortable so far as it goes. Benjamin has one-sixth of that, and becomes my own son, to be received and treated by you as your own brother, or he goes."

Mary hid her face in her hands. Adam walked to the window and looked out; but the other three broke out into a sudden, hurried clamor, strangely at variance with their usual staid demeanor.

"Oh, father, we couldn't let him go!"

"Why, father, I can't think what you mean!"

"I'm sure, sir, we never thought of such a thing as sending him away. Why, he's our Ben."

"Good enough little kid, only mischievous."

"Needs a little governing, that's all. Mary spoils him; no harm in him, not a mite."

"And the lovingest little soul! the minute he found that Kitty's paw was cut, he sat down and cried—"

"I guess if Benny went, I'd go after him pretty quick!" said Joseph, who had been loudest in his complaint against the child.

Mary looked up and smiled through her tears. "Joe, your heart is in the right place!" she said. "I finished your shirts this morning, dear; I'm going to begin on your slippers to-night."

"Well, but, father—"

"Father dear, about little Benny—"

"Yes, sir—poor little Ben!"

"Go easy!" said Father Golden; and his face, as he looked from one to the other, was as bright as his name.

"Why, children, you're real excited. I don't want excitement, nor crying—Mary, daughter, I knew how you would feel, any way. I want a serious word, 'go,' or 'stay,' from each one of you; a word that will last your lives long. I'll begin with the youngest, because that was your mother's way. She always said the youngest was nearest heaven. Joseph, what is your word about little Benjamin?"

"Stay, of course!" cried Joe. "Benny does tease me, but I should be nowhere without him."

"Ruth! you seemed greatly tried just now. Think what you are going to say."

"Oh, of course he must stay, father. Why, the child is the life of the house. We are all so humdrum and mopy, I don't know what we should do without Benny to keep us moving."

"Mary, daughter not that I need your answer, my dear."

"He is the only child I shall ever have!" said Mary, simply.

There was silence for a moment, and all thought of the grave where her young heart had laid its treasure.

"Lemuel!"

"I've been hard on the child, Father!" said Lemuel. "He's so different from the rest of us, and he does try me. But mother loved him, and down at the bottom we all do, I guess. I say stay, too, and I'll try to be more of a brother to him from now on."

"Son Adam, I have left you the longest time to reflect," said Father Golden. "You are the oldest, and when I am gone it will be on you and Mary that the heft of the care will come. Take all the time you want, and then give us your word!"

Adam turned round; his face was very grave, but he spoke cheerfully.

"I have had time enough, Father," he said. "I was the first that heard that little voice, ten years ago, and the first, except mother, that saw the child; 'twould be strange if I were the one to send him away. He came in Christ's name, and in that name I bid him stay."

"Amen!" said Father Golden.

A silence followed; but it was broken soon by a lively whistle, shrilling out a rollicking tune; the next moment a boy came running into the room. Curly, rosy, dirty, ragged, laughing, panting, little Benjamin stood still and looked round on all the earnest, serious faces.

"What's the matter, all you folks?" he asked. "I should think you was all in meeting, and sermon just beginning. Ruth, I tied up Kitty's leg all right; and I'll dig greens to pay for the glass, Joe. Say, Bro'rer-Adam-an-Lem (Benny pronounced this as if it were one word), did you forget it was April Fool's Day? Didn't I fool you good? And say! there's a fierce breeze and my new kite's a buster. Who'll come out and fly her with me?"

"I will, Benny!" said Adam, Lemuel, Mary, Ruth, and Joseph.

Week Eight:

ELETELEPHONY

Once there was an elephant,
Who tried to use the telephant—
No! no! I mean an elephone
Who tried to use the telephone—
(Dear me! I am not certain quite
That even now I've got it right.)

Howe'er it was, he got his trunk
Entangled in the telephunk;
The more he tried to get it free,
The louder buzzed the telephee—
(I fear I'd better drop the song
Of elephop and telephong!)

LAURA E. RICHARDS
(1850–1943)

Week Nine:
NELLY'S HOSPITAL
American Short Story

BY LOUISA MAY ALCOTT

Nelly sat beside her mother picking lint; but while her fingers flew, her eyes often looked wistfully out into the meadow, golden with buttercups, and bright with sunshine. Presently she said, rather bashfully, but very earnestly, "Mamma, I want to tell you a little plan I've made, if you'll please not laugh."

"I think I can safely promise that, my dear," said her mother, putting down her work that she might listen quite respectfully.

Nelly looked pleased, and went on confidingly,

"Since brother Will came home with his lame foot, and I've helped you tend him, I've heard a great deal about hospitals, and liked it very much. To-day I said I wanted to go and be a nurse, like Aunt Mercy; but Will laughed, and told me I'd better begin by nursing sick birds and butterflies and pussies before I tried to take care of men. I did not like to be made fun of, but I've been thinking that it would be very pleasant to have a little hospital all my own, and be a nurse in it, because, if I took pains, so many pretty creatures might be made well, perhaps. Could I, mamma?"

Her mother wanted to smile at the idea, but did not, for Nelly looked up with her heart and eyes so full of tender compassion, both for the unknown men for whom her little hands had done their best, and for the smaller sufferers nearer home, that she stroked the shining head, and answered readily: "Yes, Nelly, it will be a proper charity for such a young Samaritan, and you may learn much if you are in earnest. You must study how to feed and nurse your little patients, else your pity will do no good, and your hospital become a prison. I will help you, and Tony shall be your surgeon."

"O mamma, how good you always are to me! Indeed, I am in truly earnest; I will learn, I will be kind, and may I go now and begin?"

"You may, but tell me first where will you have your hospital?"

"In my room, mamma; it is so snug and sunny, and I never should forget it there," said Nelly.

"You must not forget it anywhere. I think that plan will not do. How would you like to find caterpillars walking in your bed, to hear sick pussies mewing in the night, to have beetles clinging to your clothes, or see mice, bugs, and birds tumbling downstairs whenever the door was open?" said her mother.

Nelly laughed at that thought a minute, then clapped her hands, and cried: "Let us have the old summer-house! My doves only use the upper part, and it would be so like Frank in the storybook. Please say yes again, mamma."

Her mother did say yes, and, snatching up her hat, Nelly ran to find Tony, the gardener's son, a pleasant lad of twelve, who was Nelly's favorite playmate. Tony pronounced the plan a "jolly" one, and, leaving his work, followed his young mistress to the summer-house, for she could not wait one minute.

"What must we do first?" she asked, as they stood looking in at the dusty room, full of garden tools, bags of seeds, old flower-pots, and watering-cans.

"Clear out the rubbish, miss," answered Tony.

"Here it goes, then," and Nelly began bundling everything out in such haste that she broke two flower-pots, scattered all the squash-seeds, and brought a pile of rakes and hoes clattering down about her ears.

"Just wait a bit, and let me take the lead, miss. You hand me things, I'll pile 'em in the barrow and wheel 'em off to the barn; then it will save time, and be finished up tidy."

Nelly did as he advised, and very soon nothing but dust remained.

"What next?" she asked, not knowing in the least.

"I'll sweep up while you see if Polly can come and scrub the room out. It ought to be done before you stay here, let alone the patients."

"So it had," said Nelly, looking very wise all of a sudden. "Will says the wards—that means the rooms, Tony—are scrubbed every day or two, and kept very clean, and well venti-something—I can't say it; but it means having a plenty of air come in. I can clean windows while Polly mops, and then we shall soon be done." Away she ran, feeling very busy and important. Polly came, and very soon the room looked like another place. The four latticed windows were set wide open, so the sunshine came dancing through the vines that grew outside, and curious roses peeped in to see what frolic was afoot. The walls shone white again, for not a spider dared to stay; the wide seat which encircled the room was dustless now,—the floor as nice as willing hands could make it; and the south wind blew away all musty odors with its fragrant breath.

"How fine it looks!" cried Nelly, dancing on the doorstep, lest a foot-print should mar the still damp floor.

"I'd almost like to fall sick for the sake of staying here," said Tony, admiringly. "Now, what sort of beds are you going to have, miss?"

"I suppose it won't do to put butterflies and toads and worms into beds like the real soldiers where Will was?" answered Nelly, looking anxious.

Tony could hardly help shouting at the idea; but, rather than trouble his little mistress, he said very soberly: "I'm afraid they wouldn't lay easy, not being used to it. Tucking up a butterfly would about kill him; the worms would be apt to get lost among the bed-clothes; and the toads would tumble out the first thing."

"I shall have to ask mamma about it. What will you do while I'm gone?" said Nelly, unwilling that a moment should be lost.

"I'll make frames for nettings to the windows, else the doves will come in and eat up the sick people.

"I think they will know that it is a hospital, and be too kind to hurt or frighten their neighbors," began Nelly; but as she spoke, a plump white dove walked in, looked about with its red-ringed eyes, and quietly pecked up a tiny bug that had just ventured out from the crack where it had taken refuge when the deluge came.

"Yes, we must have the nettings. I'll ask mamma for some lace," said Nelly, when she saw that; and, taking her pet dove on her shoulder, told it about her hospital as she went toward the house; for, loving all little creatures as she did, it grieved her to have any harm befall even the least or plainest of them. She had a sweet child-fancy that her playmates understood her language as she did theirs, and that birds, flowers, animals, and insects felt for her the same affection which she felt for them. Love always makes friends, and nothing seemed to fear the gentle child; but welcomed her like a little sun who shone alike on all, and never suffered an eclipse.

She was gone some time, and when she came back her mind was full of new plans, one hand full of rushes, the other of books, while over her head floated the lace, and a bright green ribbon hung across her arm.

"Mamma says that the best beds will be little baskets, boxes, cages, and any sort of thing that suits the patients; for each will need different care and food and medicine. I have not baskets enough, so, as I cannot have pretty white beds, I am going to braid pretty green nests for my patients, and, while I do it, mamma thought you'd read to me the pages she has marked, so that we may begin right."

"Yes, miss; I like that. But what is the ribbon for?" asked Tony.

"O, that's for you. Will says that, if you are to be an army surgeon, you must have a green band on your arm; so I got this to tie on when we play hospital."

Tony let her decorate the sleeve of his gray jacket, and when the nettings were done, the welcome books were opened and enjoyed. It was a happy time, sitting in the sunshine, with leaves pleasantly astir all about them, doves cooing overhead, and flowers sweetly gossiping together through the summer afternoon. Nelly wove her smooth, green rushes. Tony pored over his pages, and both found something better than fairy legends in the family histories of insects, birds, and beasts. All manner of wonders appeared, and were explained to them, till Nelly felt as if a new world had been given her, so full of beauty, interest, and pleasure that she never could be tired of studying it. Many of these things were not strange to Tony, because, born among plants, he had grown up with them as if they were brothers and sisters, and the sturdy, brown-faced boy had learned many lessons which no poet or philosopher could have taught him, unless he had become as child-like as himself, and studied from the same great book.

When the baskets were done, the marked pages all read, and the sun began to draw his rosy curtains round him before smiling "Good night," Nelly ranged the green beds round the room, Tony put in the screens, and the hospital was ready. The little nurse was so excited that she could hardly eat her supper, and directly afterwards ran up to tell Will how well she had succeeded with the first part of her enterprise. Now brother Will was a brave young officer, who had fought stoutly and done his duty like a man. But when lying weak and wounded at home, the cheerful courage which had led him safely through many dangers seemed to have deserted him, and he was often gloomy, sad, or fretful, because he longed to be at his post again, and time passed very slowly. This troubled his mother, and made Nelly wonder why he found lying in a pleasant room so much harder than fighting battles or making weary marches. Anything that interested and amused him was very welcome, and when Nelly, climbing on the arm of his sofa, told her plans, mishaps, and successes, he laughed out more heartily than he had done for many a day, and his thin face began to twinkle with fun as it used to do so long ago. That pleased Nelly, and she chatted like any affectionate little magpie, till Will was really interested; for when one is ill, small things amuse.

"Do you expect your patients to come to you, Nelly?" he asked.

"No, I shall go and look for them. I often see poor things suffering in the garden, and the wood, and always feel as if they ought to be taken care of, as people are."

"You won't like to carry insane bugs, lame toads, and convulsive kittens in your hands, and they would not stay on a stretcher if you had one. You should have an ambulance and be a branch of the Sanitary Commission," said Will.

Nelly had often heard the words, but did not quite understand what they meant. So Will told her of that great never-failing charity, to which thousands owe their lives; and the child listened with lips apart, eyes often full, and so much love and admiration in her heart that she could find no words in which to tell it. When her brother paused, she said earnestly: "Yes, I will be a Sanitary. This little cart of mine shall be my amb'lance, and I'll never let my water-barrels go empty, never drive too fast, or be rough with my poor passengers, like some of the men you tell about. Does this look like an ambulance, Will?"

"Not a bit, but it shall, if you and mamma like to help me. I want four long bits of cane, a square of white cloth, some pieces of thin wood, and the gum-pot," said Will, sitting up to examine the little cart, feeling like a boy again as he took out his knife and began to whittle. Upstairs and downstairs ran Nelly till all necessary materials were collected, and almost breathlessly she watched her brother arch the canes over the cart, cover them with the cloth, and fit an upper shelf of small compartments, each lined with cotton-wool to serve as beds for wounded insects, lest they should hurt one another or jostle out. The lower part was left free for any larger creatures which Nelly might find. Among her toys she had a tiny cask which only needed a peg to be water-tight; this was filled and fitted in before, because, as the small sufferers needed no seats, there was no place for it behind, and, as Nelly was both horse and driver, it was more convenient in front. On each side of it stood a box of stores. In one were minute rollers, as bandages are called, a few bottles not yet filled, and a wee doll's jar of cold-cream, because Nelly could not feel that her outfit was complete without a medicine-chest. The other box was full of crumbs, bits of sugar, bird-seed, and grains of wheat and corn, lest any famished stranger should die for want of food before she got it home. Then mamma painted "U.S. San. Com." in bright letters on the cover, and Nelly received her charitable plaything with a long sigh of satisfaction.

"Nine o'clock already. Bless me, what a short evening this has been," exclaimed Will, as Nelly came to give him her good-night kiss.

"And such a happy one," she answered.

"Thank you very, very much, dear Will. I only wish my little amb'lance was big enough for you to go in,—I'd so like to give you the first ride."

"Nothing I should like better, if it were possible, though I've a prejudice against ambulances in general. But as I cannot ride, I'll try and hop out to your hospital to-morrow, and see how you get on,"— which was a great deal for Captain Will to say, because he had been too listless to leave his sofa for several days.

That promise sent Nelly happily away to bed, only stopping to pop her head out of the window to see if it was likely to be a fair day to-morrow, and to tell Tony about the new plan as he passed below.

"Where shall you go to look for your first load of sick folks, miss?" he asked.

"All round the garden first, then through the grove, and home across the brook. Do you think I can find any patients so?" said Nelly.

"I know you will. Good night, miss," and Tony walked away with a merry look on his face, that Nelly would not have understood if she had seen it.

Up rose the sun bright and early, and up rose Nurse Nelly almost as early and as bright. Breakfast was taken in a great hurry, and before the dew was off the grass this branch of the S. C. was all astir. Papa, mamma, big brother and baby sister, men and maids, all looked out to see the funny little ambulance depart, and nowhere in all the summer fields was there a happier child than Nelly, as she went smiling down the garden path, where tall flowers kissed her as she passed and every blithe bird seemed singing a "Good speed!"

"How I wonder what I shall find first," she thought, looking sharply on all sides as she went. Crickets chirped, grasshoppers leaped, ants worked busily at their subterranean houses, spiders spun shining webs from twig to twig, bees were coming for their bags of gold, and butter-flies had just begun their holiday. A large white one alighted on the top of the ambulance, walked over the inscription as if spelling it letter by letter, then floated away from flower to flower, like one carrying the good news far and wide.

"Now every one will know about the hospital and be glad to see me coming," thought Nelly. And indeed it seemed so, for just then a black-bird, sitting on a garden wall, burst out with a song full of musical joy, Nelly's kitten came running after to stare at the wagon and rub her soft side against it, a bright-eyed toad looked out from his cool bower among the lily-leaves, and at that minute Nelly found her first patient. In one of the dewy cobwebs hanging from a shrub near by sat a fat black and yellow spider, watching a fly whose delicate wings were just caught in the net. The poor fly buzzed pitifully, and struggled so hard that the whole web shook: but the more he struggled, the more he entangled himself, and the fierce spider was preparing to descend that it might weave a shroud about its prey, when a little finger broke the threads and lifted the fly safely into the palm of a hand, where he lay faintly humming his thanks.

Nelly had heard much about contrabands, knew who they were, and was very much interested in them; so, when she freed the poor black fly she played he was her contraband, and felt glad that her first patient was one that needed help so much. Carefully brushing away as much of the web as she could, she left small Pompey, as she named him, to free his own legs, lest her clumsy fingers should hurt him; then she laid him in one of the soft beds with a grain or two of sugar if he needed refreshment, and bade him rest and recover from his fright, remembering that he was at liberty to fly away whenever he liked, because she had no wish to make a slave of him.

Feeling very happy over this new friend, Nelly went on singing softly as she walked, and presently she found a pretty caterpillar dressed in brown fur, although the day was warm. He lay so still she thought him dead, till he rolled himself into a ball as she touched him.

"I think you are either faint from the heat of this thick coat of yours, or that you are going to make a cocoon of yourself, Mr. Fuzz," said Nelly.

"Now I want to see you turn into a butterfly, so I shall take you, and if you get lively again I will let you go. I shall play that you have given out on a march, as the soldiers sometimes do, and been left behind for the Sanitary people to see to."

In went sulky Mr. Fuzz, and on trundled the ambulance till a golden green rose-beetle was discovered, lying on his back kicking as if in a fit.

"Dear me, what shall I do for him?" thought Nelly. "He acts as baby did when she was so ill, and mamma put her in a warm bath. I haven't got my little tub here, or any hot water, and I'm afraid the beetle would not like it if I had. Perhaps he has pain in his stomach; I'll turn him over, and pat his back, as nurse does baby's when she cries for pain like that."

She set the beetle on his legs, and did her best to comfort him; but he was evidently in great distress, for he could not walk, and instead of lifting his emerald overcoat, and spreading the wings that lay underneath, be turned over again, and kicked more violently than before. Not knowing what to do, Nelly put him into one of her soft nests for Tony to cure if possible. She found no more patients in the garden except a dead bee, which she wrapped in a leaf, and took home to bury. When she came to the grove, it was so green and cool she longed to sit and listen to the whisper of the pines, and watch the larch-tassels wave in the wind. But, recollecting her charitable errand, she went rustling along the pleasant path till she came to another patient, over which she stood considering several minutes before she could decide whether it was best to take it to her hospital, because it was a little gray snake, with a bruised tail. She knew it would not hurt her, yet she was afraid of it; she thought it pretty, yet could not like it; she pitied its pain, yet shrunk from helping it, for it had a fiery eye, and a keep quivering tongue, that looked as if longing to bite.

"He is a rebel, I wonder if I ought to be good to him," thought Nelly, watching the reptile writhe with pain. "Will said there were sick rebels in his hospital, and one was very kind to him. It says, too, in my little book, 'Love your enemies.' I think snakes are mine, but I guess I'll try and love him because God made him. Some boy will kill him if I leave him here, and then perhaps his mother will be very sad about it. Come, poor worm, I wish to help you, so be patient, and don't frighten me."

Then Nelly laid her little handkerchief on the ground, and with a stick gently lifted the wounded snake upon it, and, folding it together, laid it in the ambulance. She was thoughtful after that, and so busy puzzling her young head about the duty of loving those who hate us, and being kind to those who are disagreeable or unkind, that she went through the rest of the wood quite forgetful of her work. A soft "Queek, queek!" made her look up and listen. The sound came from the long meadow-grass, and, bending it carefully back, she found a half-fledged bird, with one wing trailing on the ground, and its eyes dim with pain or hunger.

Illustration by unknown illustrator for Louisa May Alcott in "Nelly's Hospital," *Our Young Folks* (Boston: Ticknor and Fields, 1865).

"You darling thing, did you fall out of your nest and hurt your wing?" cried Nelly, looking up into the single tree that stood near by. No nest was to be seen, no parent birds hovered overhead, and little

Robin could only tell its troubles in that mournful "Queek, queek, queek!"

Nelly ran to get both her chests, and, sitting down beside the bird, tried to feed it. To her joy it ate crumb after crumb, as if it were half starved, and soon fluttered nearer a confiding fearlessness that made her very proud. Soon baby Robin seemed quite comfortable, his eye brightened, he "queeked" no more, and but for the drooping wing would have been himself again. With one of her bandages Nelly bound both wings closely to his sides for fear he should hurt himself by trying to fly; and though he seemed amazed at her proceedings, he behaved very well, only staring at her, and ruffling up his few feathers in a funny way that made her laugh. Then she had to discover some way of accommodating her two larger patients so that neither should hurt nor alarm the other. A bright thought came to her after much pondering. Carefully lifting the handkerchief, she pinned the two ends to the roof of the cart, and there swung little Forked-tongue, while Rob lay easily below.

By this time, Nelly began to wonder how it happened that she found so many more injured things than ever before. But it never entered her innocent head that Tony had searched the wood and meadow before she was up, and laid most of these creatures ready to her hands, that she might not be disappointed. She had not yet lost her faith in fairies, so she fancied they too belonged to her small sisterhood, and presently it did really seem impossible to doubt that the good folk had been at work.

Coming to the bridge that crossed the brook, she stopped a moment to watch the water ripple over the bright pebbles, the ferns bend down to drink, and the funny tadpoles frolic in quieter nooks, where the sun shone, and the dragon-flies swung among the rushes. When Nelly turned to go on, her blue eyes opened wide, and the handle of the ambulance dropped with a noise that caused a stout frog to skip into the water heels over head. Directly in the middle of the bridge was a pretty green tent, made of two tall burdock leaves. The stems were stuck into cracks between the boards, the tips were pinned together with a thorn, and one great buttercup nodded in the doorway like a sleepy sentinel. Nelly stared and smiled, listened, and looked about on every side. Nothing was seen but the quiet meadow and the shady grove, nothing was heard but the babble of the brook and the cheery music of the bobolinks.

"Yes," said Nelly softly to herself, "that is a fairy tent, and in it I may find a baby elf sick with whooping-cough or scarlet-fever. How splendid it would be! only I could never nurse such a dainty thing."

Stooping eagerly, she peeped over the buttercup's drowsy head, and saw what seemed a tiny cock of hay. She had no time to feel disappointed, for the haycock began to stir, and, looking nearer, she beheld two silvery gray mites, who wagged wee tails, and stretched themselves as if they had just waked up. Nelly knew that they were young field-mice, and rejoiced over them, feeling rather relieved that no fairy had appeared, though she still believed them to have had a hand in the matter.

"I shall call the mice my Babes in the Wood, because they are lost and covered up with leaves," said Nelly, as she laid them in her snuggest bed, where they nestled close together, and fell fast asleep again.

Being very anxious to get home, that she might tell her adventures, and show how great was the need of a sanitary commission in that region, Nelly marched proudly up the avenue, and, having displayed her load, hurried to the hospital, where another applicant was waiting for her. On the step of the door lay a large turtle, with one claw gone, and on his back was pasted a bit of paper, with his name,—"Commodore Waddle, U.S.N." Nelly knew this was a joke of Will's, but welcomed the ancient mariner, and called Tony to help her get him in.

All that morning they were very busy settling the new-comers, for both people and books had to be consulted before they could decide what diet and treatment was best for each. The winged contraband had taken Nelly at her word, and flown away on the journey home. Little Rob was put in a large cage, where he could use his legs, yet not injure his lame wing. Forked-tongue lay under a wire cover, on sprigs of fennel, for the gardener said that snakes were fond of it. The Babes in the Wood were put to bed in one of the rush baskets, under a cotton-wool coverlet. Greenback, the beetle, found ease for his unknown aches in the warm heart of a rose, where he sunned himself all day. The Commodore was made happy in a tub of water, grass, and stones, and Mr. Fuzz was put in a well-ventilated glass box to decide whether he would be a cocoon or not.

Tony had not been idle while his mistress was away, and he showed her the hospital garden he had made close by, in which were cabbage, nettle, and mignonette plants for the butterflies, flowering herbs for the bees, chick-weed and hemp for the birds, catnip for the pussies, and plenty of room left for whatever other patients might need. In the afternoon, while Nelly did her task at lint-picking, talking busily to Will as she worked, and interesting him in her affairs, Tony cleared a pretty spot in the grove for the burying-ground, and made ready some small bits of slate on which to write the names of those who died. He did not have it ready an hour too soon, for at sunset two little graves were needed, and Nurse Nelly shed tender tears for her first losses as she laid the motherless mice in one smooth hollow, and the gray-coated rebel in the other. She had learned to care for him already, and when she found him dead, was very glad she had been kind to him, hoping that he knew it, and died happier in her hospital than all alone in the shadowy wood.

The rest of Nelly's patients prospered, and of the many added afterward few died, because of Tony's skilful treatment and her own faithful care. Every morning when the day proved fair the little ambulance went out upon its charitable errand; every afternoon Nelly worked for the human sufferers whom she loved; and every evening brother Will read aloud to her from useful books, showed her wonders with his microscope, or prescribed remedies for the patients, whom he soon knew by name and took much interest in. It was Nelly's holiday; but, though she studied no lessons, she learned much, and unconsciously made her pretty play both an example and a rebuke for others.

At first it seemed a childish pastime, and people laughed. But there was something in the familiar words "sanitary," "hospital," and "ambulance" that made them pleasant sounds to many ears. As reports of Nelly's work went through the neighborhood, other children came to see and copy her design. Rough lads looked ashamed when in her wards they found harmless creatures hurt by them, and going out they said among themselves, "We won't stone birds, chase butterflies, and drown the girls' little cats any more, though we won't tell them so." And most of the lads kept their word so well that people said there never had been so many birds before as all that summer haunted wood and field. Tender-hearted playmates brought their pets to be cured; even busy farmers bad a friendly word for the small charity, which reminded them so sweetly of the great one which should never be forgotten; lonely mothers sometimes looked out with wet eyes as the little ambulance went by, recalling thoughts of absent sons who might be journeying painfully to some far-off hospital, where brave women waited to tend them with hands as willing, hearts as tender, as those the gentle child gave to her self-appointed task.

At home the charm worked also. No more idle days for Nelly, or fretful ones for Will, because the little sister would not neglect the helpless creatures so dependent upon her, and the big brother was ashamed to complain after watching the patience of these lesser sufferers, and merrily said he would try to bear his own wound as quietly and bravely as the "Commodore" bore his. Nelly never knew how much good she had done Captain Will till he went away again in the early autumn. Then he thanked her for it, and though she cried for joy and sorrow she never forgot it, because he left something behind him which always pleasantly reminded her of the double success her little hospital had won.

When Will was gone and she had prayed softly in her heart that God would keep him safe and bring him home again, she dried her tears and went away to find comfort in the place where he had spent so many happy hours with her. She had not been there before that day, and when she reached the door she stood quite still and wanted very much to cry again, far something beautiful had happened. She had often asked Will for a motto for her hospital, and he had promised to find her one. She thought he had forgotten it; but even in the hurry of that busy day he had found time to do more than keep his word, while Nelly sat indoors, lovingly brightening the tarnished buttons on the blue coat that had seen so many battles.

Above the roof, where the doves cooed in the sun, now rustled a white flag with the golden "S. C." shining on it as the wind tossed it to and fro. Below, on the smooth panel of the door, a skilful pencil had drawn two arching ferns, in whose soft shadow, poised upon a mushroom, stood a little figure of Nurse Nelly, and underneath it another of Dr. Tony bottling medicine, with spectacles upon his nose. Both hands of the miniature Nelly were outstretched, as if beckoning to a train of insects, birds, and beasts, which was so long that it not only circled round the lower rim of this fine sketch, but dwindled in the distance to mere dots and lines. Such merry conceits as one found there! A mouse bringing the tail it had lost in some cruel trap, a dor-bug with a shade over its eyes, an invalid butterfly carried in a tiny litter by long-legged spiders, a fat frog with gouty feet hopping upon crutches, Jenny Wren sobbing in a nice handkerchief, as she brought dear dead Cock Robin to be restored to life. Rabbits, lambs, cats, calves, and turtles, all came trooping up to be healed by the benevolent little maid who welcomed them so heartily.

Nelly laughed at these comical mites till the tears ran down her cheeks, and thought she never could be tired of looking at them. But presently she saw four lines clearly printed underneath her picture, and her childish face grew sweetly serious as she read the words of a great poet, which Will had made both compliment and motto:—

> "He prayeth best who loveth best
> All things, both great and small;
> For the dear God who loveth us,
> He made and loveth all."

"There on a high stool in a high tower on a high hill sits the Head Spotter of the Weather Makers." Illustration by Maud and Miska Petersham for Carl Sandburg in *Rootabaga Stories* (New York: Harcourt, Brace & Co., c. 1922).

Week Nine:

How the Animals Lost Their Tails and Got Them Back Traveling From Philadelphia to Medicine Hat

American Short Story

BY CARL SANDBURG

Far up in North America, near the Saskatchewan river, in the Winnipeg wheat country, not so far from the town of Moose Jaw named for the jaw of a moose shot by a hunter there, up where the blizzards and the chinooks begin, where nobody works unless they have to and they nearly all have to, there stands the place known as Medicine Hat.

And there on a high stool in a high tower on a high hill sits the Head Spotter of the Weather Makers.

When the animals lost their tails it was because the Head Spotter of the Weather Makers at Medicine Hat was careless.

The tails of the animals were stiff and dry because for a long while there was dusty dry weather. Then at last came rain. And the water from the sky poured on the tails of the animals and softened them.

Then the chilly chills came whistling with icy mittens and they froze all the tails stiff. A big wind blew up and blew and blew till all the tails of the animals blew off.

It was easy for the fat stub hogs with their fat stub tails. But it was not so easy for the blue fox who uses his tail to help him when he runs, when he eats, when he walks or talks, when he makes pictures or writes letters in the snow or when he puts a snack of bacon meat with stripes of fat and lean to hide till he wants it under a big rock by a river.

It was easy enough for the rabbit who has long ears and no tail at all except a white thumb of cotton. But it was hard for the yellow flongboo who at night lights up his house in a hollow tree with his fire yellow torch of a tail. It is hard for the yellow flongboo to lose his tail because it lights up his way when he sneaks at night on the prairie, sneaking up on the flangwayers, the hippers and hangjasts, so good to eat.

The animals picked a committee of representatives to represent them in a parleyhoo to see what steps could be taken by talking to do something. There were sixty-six representatives on the committee and they decided to call it the Committee of Sixty-Six. It was a distinguished committee and when they all sat together holding their mouths under their noses (just like a distinguished committee) and blinking their eyes up over their noses and cleaning their ears and scratching themselves under the chin looking thoughtful (just like a distinguished committee) then anybody would say just to look at them, "This must be quite a distinguished committee."

Of course, they would all have looked more distinguished if they had had their tails on. If the big wavy streak of a blue tail blows off behind a blue fox, he doesn't look near so distinguished. Or, if the long yellow torch of a tail blows off behind a yellow flongboo, he doesn't look so distinguished as he did before the wind blew.

So the Committee of Sixty-Six had a meeting and a parleyhoo to decide what steps could be taken by talking to do something. For chairman they picked an old flongboo who was an umpire and used to umpire many mix-ups. Among the flongboos he was called "the umpire of umpires," "the king of umpires," "the prince of umpires," "the peer of umpires." When there was a fight and a snag and a wrangle between two families living next-door neighbors to each other and this old flongboo was called in to umpire and to say which family was right and which family was wrong, which family started it and which family ought to stop it, he used to say, "The best umpire is the one who knows just how far to go and how far not to go." He was from Massachusetts, born near Chappaquiddick, this old flongboo, and he lived there in a horse chestnut tree six feet thick halfway between South Hadley and Northampton. And at night, before he lost his tail, he lighted up the big hollow cave inside the horse chestnut tree with his yellow torch of a tail.

After he was nominated with speeches and elected with votes to be the chairman, he stood up on the platform and took a gavel and banged with the gavel and made the Committee of Sixty-Six come to order.

"It is no picnic to lose your tail and we are here for business," he said, banging his gavel again.

A blue fox from Waco, Texas, with his ears full of dry bluebonnet leaves from a hole where he lived near the Brazos river, stood up and said, "Mr. Chairman, do I have the floor?"

"You have whatever you get away with—I get your number," said the chairman.

"I make a motion," said the blue fox from Waco, "and I move you, Sir, that this committee get on a train at Philadelphia and ride on the train till it stops and then take another train and take more trains and keep on riding till we get to Medicine Hat, near the Saskatchewan river, in the Winnipeg wheat country where the Head Spotter of the Weather Makers sits on a high stool in a high tower on a high hill spotting the weather. There we will ask him if he will respectfully let us beseech him to bring back weather that will bring back our tails. It was the weather took away our tails; it is the weather can bring back our tails."

"All in favor of the motion," said the chairman, "will clean their right ears with their right paws."

And all the blue foxes and all the yellow flongboos began cleaning their right ears with their right paws.

"All who are against the motion will clean their left ears with their left paws," said the chairman.

And all the blue foxes and all the yellow flongboos began cleaning their left ears with their left paws.

"The motion is carried both ways—"it is a razmataz," said the chairman. "Once again, all in favor of the motion will stand up on the toes of their hind legs and stick their noses straight up in the air." And all the blue foxes and all the yellow flongboos stood up on the toes of their hind legs and stuck their noses straight up in the air.

"And now," said the chairman, "all who are against the motion will stand on the top and the apex of their heads, stick their hind legs straight up in the air, and make a noise like a woof woof."

And then not one of the blue foxes and not one of the yellow flongboos stood on the top and the apex of his head nor stuck his hind legs up in the air nor made a noise like a woof woof.

"The motion is carried and this is no picnic," said the chairman.

So the committee went to Philadelphia to get on a train to ride on.

"Would you be so kind as to tell us the way to the union depot," the chairman asked a policeman. It was the first time a flongboo ever spoke to a policeman on the streets of Philadelphia.

"It pays to be polite," said the policeman.

"May I ask you again if you would kindly direct us to the union depot? We wish to ride on a train," said the flongboo.

"Polite persons and angry persons are different kinds," said the policeman.

The flongboo's eyes changed their lights and a slow torch of fire sprang out behind where his tail used to be. And speaking to the policeman, he said, "Sir, I must inform you, publicly and respectfully, that we are The Committee of Sixty-Six. We are honorable and distinguished representatives from places your honest and ignorant geography never told you about. This committee is going to ride on the cars to Medicine Hat near the Saskatchewan river in the Winnipeg wheat country where the blizzards and chinooks begin. We have a special message and a secret errand for the Head Spotter of the Weather Makers."

"I am a polite friend of all respectable people—that is why I wear this star to arrest people who are not respectable," said the policeman, touching with his pointing finger the silver and nickel star fastened with a safety pin on his blue uniform coat.

"This is the first time ever in the history of the United States that a committee of sixty-six blue foxes and flongboos has ever visited a city in the United States," insinuated the flongboo.

"I beg to be mistaken," finished the policeman. "The union depot is under that clock." And he pointed to a clock near by.

"I thank you for myself, I thank you for the Committee of Sixty-Six, I thank you for the sake of all the animals in the United States who have lost their tails," finished the chairman.

Over to the Philadelphia union depot they went, all sixty-six, half blue foxes, half flongboos. As they pattered pitty-pat, pitty-pat, each with feet and toenails, ears and hair, everything but tails, into the Philadelphia union depot, they had nothing to say. And yet though they had nothing to say, the passengers in the union depot waiting for trains thought they had something to say and were saying it. So the passengers in the union depot waiting for trains listened. But with all their listening the passengers never heard the blue foxes and yellow flongboos say anything.

"They are saying it to each other in some strange language from where they belong," said one passenger waiting for a train.

"They have secrets to keep among each other, and never tell us," said another passenger.

"We will find out all about it reading the newspapers upside down tomorrow morning," said a third passenger.

Then the blue foxes and the yellow flongboos pattered pitty-pat, pitty-pat, each with feet and toenails, ears and hair, everything except tails, pattered scritch scratch over the stone floors out into the train shed. They climbed into a special smoking car hooked on ahead of the engine.

"This car hooked on ahead of the engine was put on special for us so we will always be ahead and we will get there before the train does," said the chairman to the committee.

The train ran out of the train shed. It kept on the tracks and never left the rails. It came to the Horseshoe Curve near Altoona where the tracks bend like a big horseshoe. Instead of going around the long winding bend of the horseshoe tracks up and around the mountains, the train acted different. The train jumped off the tracks down into the valley and cut across in a straight line on a cut-off, jumped on the tracks again and went on toward Ohio.

The conductor said, "If you are going to jump the train off the tracks, tell us about it beforehand."

"When we lost our tails nobody told us about it beforehand," said the old flongboo umpire.

Two baby blue foxes, the youngest on the committee, sat on the front platform. Mile after mile of chimneys went by. Four hundred smokestacks stood in a row and tubs on tubs of sooty black soot marched out.

"This is the place where the black cats come to be washed," said the first baby blue fox.

"I believe your affidavit," said the second blue fox.

Crossing Ohio and Indiana at night the flongboos took off the roof of the car. The conductor told them, "I must have an explanation." "It was between us and the stars," they told him.

The train ran into Chicago. That afternoon there were pictures upside down in the newspapers showing the blue foxes and the yellow flongboos climbing telephone poles standing on their heads eating pink ice cream with iron axes.

Each blue fox and yellow flongboo got a newspaper for himself and each one looked long and careful upside down to see how he looked in the picture in the newspaper climbing a telephone pole standing on his head eating pink ice cream with an iron ax.

Crossing Minnesota the sky began to fill with the snow ghosts of Minnesota snow weather. Again the foxes and flongboos lifted the roof off the car, telling the conductor they would rather wreck the train than miss the big show of the snow ghosts of the first Minnesota snow weather of the winter.

Some went to sleep but the two baby blue foxes stayed up all night watching the snow ghosts and telling snow ghost stories to each other.

Early in the night the first baby blue fox said to the second, "Who are the snow ghosts the ghosts of?" The second baby blue fox answered, "Everybody who makes a snowball, a snowman, a snow fox or a snow fish or a snow pattycake, everybody has a snow ghost."

And that was only the beginning of their talk. It would take a big book to tell all that the two baby foxes told each other that night about the Minnesota snow ghosts, because they sat up all night telling old stories their fathers and mothers and grandfathers and grandmothers told them, and making up new stories never heard before about where the snow ghosts go on Christmas morning and how the snow ghosts watch the New Year in.

Somewhere between Winnipeg and Moose Jaw, somewhere it was they stopped the train, and all ran out in the snow where the white moon was shining down a valley of birch trees. It was the Snowbird Valley where all the snowbirds of Canada come early in the winter and make their snow shoes.

At last they came to Medicine Hat, near the Saskatchewan River, where the blizzards and the chinooks begin, where nobody works unless they have to and they nearly all have to. There they ran in the snow till they came to the place where the Head Spotter of the Weather Makers sits on a high stool in a high tower on a high hill watching the weather.

"Let loose another big wind to blow back our tails to us, let loose a big freeze to freeze our tails onto us again, and so let us get back our lost tails," they said to the Head Spotter of the Weather Makers.

Which was just what he did, giving them exactly what they wanted, so they all went back home satisfied, the blue foxes each with a big wavy brush of a tail to help him when he runs, when he eats, when he walks or talks, when he makes pictures or writes letters in the snow or when he puts a snack of bacon meat with stripes of fat and lean to hide till he wants it under a big rock by the river—and the yellow flogboos each with a long yellow torch of a tail to light up his home in a hollow tree or to the prairie, sneaking up on the flangwayer, the hipper or the hangjast.

Week Nine:
FOG

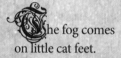The fog comes
on little cat feet.

It sits looking
over harbor and city
on silent haunches
and then moves on.

CARL SANDBURG
(1878–1967)

Fog, painted by Caspar David Freidrich in 1807.

"But it was *my* wishbone." Illustration by Lynn Bogue Hunt in *The Children's Book of Thanksgiving Stories,* edited by Asa Don Dickinson (Garden City and New York: Doubleday, Page & Co., 1915).

Week Ten:

THE FIRST THANKSGIVING

American Short Story

BY ALBERT F. BLAISDELL AND FRANCIS K. BALL

All through the first summer and the early part of autumn the Pilgrims were busy and happy. They had planted and cared for their first fields of corn. They had found wild strawberries in the meadows, raspberries on the hillsides, and wild grapes in the woods.

In the forest just back of the village wild turkeys and deer were easily shot. In the shallow waters of the bay there was plenty of fish, clams, and lobsters.

The summer had been warm, with a good deal of rain and much sunshine; and so when the autumn came there was a fine crop of corn.

"Let us gather the fruits of our first labours and rejoice together," said Governor Bradford.

"Yes," said Elder Brewster, "let us take a day upon which we may thank God for all our blessings, and invite to it our Indian friends who have been so kind to us."

The Pilgrims said that one day was not enough; so they planned to have a celebration for a whole week. This took place most likely in October.

The great Indian chief, Massasoit, came with ninety of his bravest warriors, all gayly dressed in deerskins, feathers, and foxtails, with their faces smeared with red, white, and yellow paint.

As a sign of rank, Massasoit wore round his neck a string of bones and a bag of tobacco. In his belt he carried a long knife. His face was painted red, and his hair was so daubed with oil that Governor Bradford said he "looked greasily."

Now there were only eleven buildings in the whole of Plymouth village, four log storehouses and seven little log dwelling-houses; so the Indian guests ate and slept out of doors. This was no matter, for it was one of those warm weeks in the season we call Indian summer.

To supply meat for the occasion four men had already been sent out to hunt wild turkeys. They killed enough in one day to last the whole company almost a week.

Massasoit helped the feast along by sending some of his best hunters into the woods. They killed five deer, which they gave to their paleface friends, that all might have enough to eat.

Under the trees were built long, rude tables on which were piled baked clams, broiled fish, roast turkey, and deer meat.

The young Pilgrim women helped serve the food to the hungry redskins.

Let us remember two of the fair girls who waited on the tables. One was Mary Chilton, who leaped from the boat at Plymouth Rock; the other was Mary Allerton. She lived for seventy-eight years after this first Thanksgiving, and of those who came over in the *Mayflower* she was the last to die.

What a merry time everybody had during that week! It may be they joked Governor Bradford about stepping into a deer trap set by the Indians and being jerked up by the leg.

How the women must have laughed as they told about the first Monday morning at Cape Cod, when they all went ashore to wash their clothes!

It must have been a big washing, for there had been no chance to do it at sea, so stormy had been the long voyage of sixty-three days. They little thought that Monday would afterward be kept as washday.

Then there was young John Howland, who in mid-ocean fell overboard but was quick enough to catch hold of a trailing rope. Perhaps after dinner he invited Elizabeth Tilley, whom he afterward married, to sail over to Clarke's Island and return by moonlight.

With them, it may be, went John Alden and Priscilla Mullins, whose love story is so sweetly told by Longfellow.

One proud mother, we may be sure, showed her bright-eyed boy, Peregrine White.

And so the fun went on. In the daytime the young men ran races, played games, and had a shooting match. Every night the Indians sang and danced for their friends; and to make things still more lively they gave every now and then a shrill war whoop that made the woods echo in the still night air.

The Indians had already learned to love and fear Captain Miles Standish. Some of them called him "Boiling Water" because he was easily made angry. Others called him "Captain Shrimp," on account of his small size.

Every morning the shrewd captain put on his armour and paraded his little company of a dozen or more soldiers; and when he fired off the cannon on Burial Hill the Indians must have felt that the English were men of might thus to harness up thunder and lightning.

During this week of fun and frolic it was a wonder if young Jack Billington did not play some prank on the Indians. He was the boy who fired off his father's gun one day, close to a keg of gunpowder, in the crowded cabin of the *Mayflower*.

The third day came. Massasoit had been well treated, and no doubt would have liked to stay longer, but he had said he could stay only three days. So the pipe of peace was silently passed around.

Then, taking their presents of glass beads and trinkets, the Indian king and his warriors said farewell to their English friends and began their long tramp through the woods to their wigwams on Mount Hope Bay.

On the last day of this Thanksgiving party the Pilgrims had a service of prayer and praise. Elder Brewster preached the first Thanksgiving sermon. After thanking God for all his goodness, he did not forget the many loved ones sleeping on the hillside.

He spoke of noble John Carver, the first governor, who had died of worry and overwork.

Nor was Rose Standish forgotten, the lovely young wife of Captain Miles Standish, whose death was caused by cold and lack of good food.

And then there was gentle Dorothy, wife of Governor Bradford, who had fallen overboard from the *Mayflower* in Provincetown harbour while her husband was coasting along the bleak shore in search of a place for a home.

The first Thanksgiving took place nearly three hundred years ago. Since that time, almost without interruption, Thanksgiving has been kept by the people of New England as the great family festival of the year. At this time children and grandchildren return to the old home, the long table is spread, and brothers and sisters, separated often by many miles, again sit side by side.

Today Thanksgiving is observed in nearly all the states of the Union, a season of sweet and blessed memories.

Week Ten:
THE PUMPKIN

Oh, greenly and fair in the lands of the sun,
The vines of the gourd and the rich melon run,
And the rock and the tree and the cottage enfold,
With broad leaves all greenness and blossoms all gold,
Like that which o'er Nineveh's prophet once grew,
While he waited to know that his warning was true,
And longed for the storm-cloud, and listened in vain
For the rush of the whirlwind and red fire-rain.

On the banks of the Xenil the dark Spanish maiden
Comes up with the fruit of the tangled vine laden;
And the Creole of Cuba laughs out to behold
Through orange-leaves shining the broad spheres of gold;
Yet with dearer delight from his home in the North,
On the fields of his harvest the Yankee looks forth,
Where crook-necks are coiling and yellow fruit shines,
And the sun of September melts down on his vines.

Ah! on Thanksgiving day, when from East and from West,
From North and from South come the pilgrim and guest,
When the gray-haired New-Englander sees round his board
The old broken links of affection restored,
When the care-wearied man seeks his mother once more,
And the worn matron smiles where the girl smiled before,
What moistens the lip and what brightens the eye ?
What calls back the past, like the rich Pumpkin pie?

Oh, fruit loved of boyhood! the old days recalling,
When wood-grapes were purpling and brown nuts were falling!
When wild, ugly faces we carved in its skin,
Glaring out through the dark with a candle within!
When we laughed round the core-heap, with hearts all in tune,
Our chair a broad pumpkin, our lantern the moon,
Telling tales of the fairy who travelled like steam,
In a pumpkin-shell coach, with two rats for her team!

JOHN GREENLEAF WHITTIER
(1807–1892)

Week Eleven:

The Baby-House

American Short Story

BY PETER PARLEY [SAMUEL GOODRICH]

Are there any of you, my young friends, so young or so ignorant as to believe that, if you might go to the beautiful toy shops, and had but money enough to buy just what toys you fancy, you should be quite happy?

You have heard of Napoleon, the great Emperor of France, and perhaps you have heard of his wife, the lovely Empress Josephine. She had a daughter, Hortense, who was married to the King of Holland, Napoleon's brother. The Queen of Holland had children, dearly beloved by their grandmother Josephine. One year, as the Christmas holidays approached, she sent for those artisans in Paris who manufacture toys, and ordered toys to be made expressly for her grandchildren, more beautiful and more costly than any that were to be bought. Her commands were obeyed—the toys arrived in Holland at the right time, and on Christmas morning were given to the children. For a little while they were enchanted; they thought they should never see enough of . doll that could speak, wild beasts that could roar and growl, and birds that could sing.

But, alas! after a few hours, they were tired of a doll that could say nothing but ma—ma, pa—pa, of beasts that growled in but one tone, and the birds that sang the same note. Before evening the toys were strewn over the floor, some broken, all neglected and deserted; and the mother, on coming into the apartment, found one of the little princes crying at a window that overlooked a court, where some poor children were merrily playing.

"Crying to-day, my son?" she exclaimed. "Oh! what would dear grandmamma say?—what are you crying for?"

"I want to go and play with those children in that pretty dirt, mamma."

This story was brought to my mind last Christmas eve. I went to see a very good neighbour of ours, Mrs. Selby, a carpenter's wife. The whole family are industrious and economical, and obliged to be so, for Mr. Selby cannot always get work in these times. He will not call them hard times. "It would be a shame to us," he says, "to call times hard when we never go hungry, and have decent clothes to cover us, and have health on our cheeks, and love in our hearts."

And, sure enough, there was no look of hard times there. The room was clean and warm. Mrs. Selby was busy over her mending basket, putting a darn here, a button in this place, and a hook and a eye there, to have all in order for Christmas morning. Her only son, Charles, was very busy with some of his father's tools in one corner; not too busy, though, to make his bow to me, and draw forward the rocking-chair. I wish I could find as good manners among our drawing-room children, as I see at Mrs. Selby's. Sarah and Lucy, the two girls, one eleven, the other ten years old, were working away by the light of a single lamp, so deeply engaged that they did not at first notice my entrance. "Where is little Nannie?" I asked. "She is gone to bed—put out of the way," replied Mrs. Selby. "Oh, mother!" exclaimed the girls. "Well, then—have not you banished her?" "Banished? No, mother—Oh! mother is only teasing us;" and they blushed and smiled.

"Here is some mystery," said I; "what is it, Sarah?" "Mother may tell if she pleases, ma'am," said Sarah. Mother was very happy to tell, for all mothers like to tell good of their children.

"You know, ma'am, the children all dote on little Nannie, she is so much younger than they—only five years old—and they had a desire to have some very pretty Christmas gift for her; but how could they, they said, with so little money as they had to spend? They have, to be sure, a little store. I make it a rule to give each a penny at the end of the week, if I see them improving in their weak point." "Weak point! what is that, Mrs. Selby?" "Why, ma'am, Charles is not always punctual at school; so I promised him that if he will not be one half minute behindhand for a week, he shall have a penny. Sarah, who is a little head over heels, gets one for making the beds and dusting neatly. And Lucy—Lucy is a careless child—for not getting a spot on her apron. On counting up Charles had fifty-one pennies Sarah forty-eight, and Lucy forty-nine."

"No, mother," said Lucy; "Sarah had forty-eight, and I forty-seven." "Ah, so it was; thank you, dear, for correcting me." "But Lucy would have had just the same as I, only she lost one penny by breaking a tea-cup, and it was such cold weather it almost broke itself."

I looked with delight at these little girls, so just and generous to one another. The mother proceeded: "Father makes it a rule, if they have been good children, to give them two shillings each, for holidays; so they had seventy-five pennies apiece."

"Enough," said I, "to make little Miss Nannie a pretty respectable present."

"Ah, indeed, if it were all for Nannie; but they gave a Christmas present to their father and to me, and to each other, and to the poor little lame child, next door; so that Nannie only comes in for a sixth part. They set their wits to work to contrive something more than their money would buy, and they determined on making a baby-house, which they were sure would please her and give her many a pleasant hour when they were gone to school. So there it stands in the corner of the room. Take away the shawl, girls, and show it to Miss ——. The shawl has been carefully kept over it, to hide it from Nanny, that she may have the pleasure of surprise to-morrow morning." The shawl was removed, and if my little readers have ever been to the theatre, and remember their pleasure when the curtain was first drawn up, they can imagine mine. The baby-house was three stories high—that is, there were three rooms, one above the other, made by placing three old wooden boxes one on the other. Old, I call them, but so they did not appear: their outsides had been well scoured, then pasted over with paper, and the gum arabic was put on the paper, and over that was nicely scattered a coating of granite-coloured smalt. The inside wall of the lower room, or kitchen, was covered with white paper, to look like fresh white-wash; the parlour and chamber walls were covered with very pretty hanging paper, given to the children by their friend, Miss Laverty, the upholsterer. The kitchen floor was spread with straw matting. Charles had made a very nice dresser for one side, and a table and a seat resembling a settee, for the other. The girls had created something in the likeness of a woman, whom they called a cook; the broom she held in one hand—they had made it admirably—and the pail in the other was Charles' handy-work. A stove, shovel, and tongs, tea-kettle and skillet, and dishes for the dresser they had spent money for. They were determined, first, to get their necessaries, Sarah said, (a wise little housewife,) if they went without everything else. The kitchen furniture, smalt and gum arabic, had cost them eighteen-pence—just half their joint stock. "Then how could you possibly furnish your parlour and chamber so beautifully?"

"Oh, that is almost all our own work, ma'am. Charlie made the frames of the chairs and sofas, and we stuffed and covered them." "But where did you get this very pretty crimson cloth to cover them, and the materials for your carpet and curtains?" The parlour carpet was made of dark cloth, with a centre piece of flowers and birds, very neatly fashioned, and sewed on. The chamber carpet was made of squares of diverse coloured cloth.

The cloth for the centre-table was neatly worked; the window curtains were strips of rich coloured cotton sewed together; the colours matched the colours of the carpet. To my question to Sarah, where she had got all these pretty materials, she replied, "Oh, ma'am, we did not buy them with money, but we bought them and paid for them with labour, as father says."

These little girls were early beginning to learn that truth in political economy, that all property is produced and obtained by labour. "Miss Laverty, the upholsteress, works up stairs—we picked hair for her, and she paid us in these pieces."

"The centre-table, bedstead, and chairs," said the mother, "and the wardrobe for the bed-chamber, Charlie made. The bed-sheets, pillows, spreads, &c., the girls made from pieces fished, as they say, out of my piece-basket. The work was all done in their play hours; their working time is not theirs, and therefore they could not give it away."

"I see," said I, looking at some very pretty pictures hanging around the parlour and chamber walls, "how these are arranged; they seem cut out of old books, pasted against pasteboard, and bound around with gilt paper; but pray tell me how this little mamma doll was bought, and the little baby in the cradle, and this pretty tea-set, and the candle-sticks, and the book-case and flower-vase on the centre-table, and the parlour stove. Charlie could make none of these things; you could not contrive them out of Miss Laverty's pieces; and surely the three sixpences left after your expenditure for the kitchen, would go very little way towards paying for them."

"To tell the truth, ma'am," said Mrs. Selby, "the girls were at their wits' ends. Miss Laverty could not afford to pay them money for their work. I had got almost as much interested in fitting up the baby-house as they, and would gladly have given them a little more money, but I had not a shilling to spare. Sarah and Lucy laid their heads together one night after they went to bed, and in the morning they came to me and told me their plan.

"We have always a pudding-pie on Sunday instead of meat. 'Can't you, mother,' said they, 'reckon up what our portion of the pie costs?— Make one just large enough for you, and my father, and Nannie, and we will eat dry bread, and then, with the money saved, added to our three sixpences, we will get what we can.' At first I thought it rather hard upon the children, but my husband and I talked it over together, and we concluded, as it was their own proposal, to let them do it. We thought it might be teaching them, ma'am, to have love, as one may say, stronger than appetite, and work their little self-denial up with their love, and industry, and ingenuity. Poor people, such as we, cannot do what rich people can, for the education of their children. But there are some things we can do, which rich people can't—our poor circumstances help us. When our children want to do a kindness, as in this matter of the baby-house, they can't run to father and mother, and get money to do it with; they are obliged to think it out, and work it out, as one may say; and I believe it is the great end of education, ma'am, to make mind, heart, and hand work."

Again I looked at the baby-house, and with real respect for the people who had furnished it. The figures on the carpet, the gay curtains, tables, chairs, &c., were all very pretty, and very suitably and neatly arranged, but they were something more,—outward forms, into which Charles, Sarah, and Lucy had breathed, a soul instinct with love, kindheartedness, diligence, and self-denial.

Now, I ask my young friends to compare the gifts of the poor carpenter's children to those of the empress. Hers cost a single order, and a great deal of money,—theirs, much labour and forethought. If the happiness produced in the two cases, to both giver and receiver, were calculated, which would be the greatest amount? And which, in reality, were the richest—the rich empress's grandchildren, or the poor carpenter's little family?

Week Eleven

A Case of Coincidence

American Short Story

by Rose Terry Cooke

She was a queer old lady, was Grandmother Grant; she was not a bit like other grandmothers; she was short and fat and rosy as a winter apple, with a great deal of snow-white hair set up in a big puff on top of her head, and eyes as black as huckleberries, always puckered up with smiles or laughter.

She never would wear a cap.

"I can't be bothered with 'em!" she said: and when Amelia Rutledge, who was determined her grandma should, as she said, "look half-way decent," made her two beautiful little mob caps, soft and fluffy, and each with a big satin bow, one lavender and one white, put on to show where the front was, Grandma never put them on right; the bow was over one ear or behind, or the cap itself was awry, and in the end she pulled them off and stuck them on a china jar in the parlor, or a tin canister on the kitchen shelf, and left them there till flies and dust ruined them.

"Amelia's as obstinate as a pig!" said the old lady: "she would have me wear 'em, and I wouldn't!"

That was all, but it was enough; not a grandchild ever made her another cap. Moreover Grandmother Grant always dressed in one

"Up the school-house hill." Illustration by staff illustrator for *Wide Awake Magazine*, Vol. 16 No. 1 (December 1882).

fashion; she had a calico dress for morning and a black silk for the afternoon, made with an old-fashioned surplice waist, with a thick plaited ruff about her throat; she sometimes tied a large white apron on, but only when she went into the kitchen; and she wore a pocket as big as three of yours, Matilda, tied on underneath and reached through a slit in her gown. Therein she kept her keys, her smelling-bottle, her pocket-book, her handkerchief and her spectacles, a bit of flagroot and some liquorice stick. I mean when I say this, that all these things belonged in her pocket, and she meant to keep them there; but it was one peculiarity of the dear old lady, that she always lost her necessary conveniences, and lost them every day.

"Maria!" she would call out to her daughter in the next room, "have you seen my spectacles?"

"No, mother; when did you have them?"

"Five minutes ago, darning Harry's stockings; but never mind, there's another pair in the basket."

In half an hour when Gerty came into her room for something she needed, Grandmother would say:

"Gerty, do look on the floor and see if my specs lie anywhere around."

Gerty couldn't find them, and then Grandma would say:

"Probably they dropped out on the grass under the window, you can see when you go down; but give me my gold pair out of my upper drawer."

And when Mrs. Maria went to call her mother down to dinner she would find her hunting all about the room, turning her cushions over, peering into the wood-basket, shaking out the silk quilt, and say "What is it you want, mother?"

"My specs, dear. I can't find one pair."

"But there are three on your head now!" and Grandma would sit down and laugh till she shook all over, as if it were the best joke in the world to push your spectacles up over the short white curls on your forehead, one pair after another, and forget all about them.

She mislaid her handkerchief still oftener. Gerty would sometimes pick up six of these useful articles in one day where the old lady dropped them as she went about the house; but

"Mrs. Maria finds the lost specs." Illustration by staff illustrator for *Wide Awake Magazine*, Vol. 16 No. 1 (December 1882).

the most troublesome of all her habits was a way she had of putting her pocket-book in some queer place every night, or if ever she left home in the day-time, and then utterly forgetting where she had secreted it from the burglars or thieves she had all her life expected.

The house she lived in was her own, but Doctor White who had married her daughter Maria, rented it of her, and the rent paid her board; she had a thousand dollars a year beside, half of which she reserved for her dress and her charities, keeping the other half for her Christmas gifts to her children and grandchildren. There were ten of these last, and the ten always needed something. Gerty White, the doctor's daughter, was twelve years old; she had three brothers: Tom, John, and Harry, all older than she was. Mrs. Rutledge, who had been Annie Grant, was a widow with three daughters—Sylvia, Amelia, and Anne, these latter two now out in society and always glad of new dresses, gloves, bonnets, ribbons, lace, and the thousand small fineries girls never have to their full satisfaction. There were Thomas Grant's two girls of thirteen and fifteen, Rosamond and Kate, and his little boy Hal, crippled in his babyhood so that he must always go on crutches, but as bright and happy as Grandma herself, and her prime favorite.

Now it was Grandma's way to draw her money out of the bank two weeks before Christmas, and go into Boston with Mrs. White to buy all the things she had previously thought over for these ten and their parents; and one winter she had made herself all ready to take the ten-o'clock train, and had just taken her pocket-book out of the drawer when she was called down-stairs to see a poor woman who had come begging for some clothes for her husband.

"Come right upstairs, Mrs. Slack," said Grandma. "I don't have many applications for men's things, so I guess there's a coat of Mr. Grant's put away in the camphor chest, and maybe a vest or so; you sit right down by my fire whilst I go up to the garret and look."

It took Grandma some time to find the clothes under all the shawls and blankets in the chest, and when she had given them to Mrs. Slack she had to hurry to the station with her daughter, and the cars being on the track they did not stop to get tickets, but were barely in time to find seats when the train rolled off. The conductor came round in a few minutes and Grandma put her hand in her pocket, suddenly turned pale, opened her big satchel and turned out all its contents, stood up and shook her dress, looked on the floor, and when Mrs. White said in amazement, "What is the matter, mother?" she answered curtly, "I've lost my pocket-book."

"Was it in your pocket?" asked Maria.

"Yes; at least I s'pose so: I certainly took it out of my drawer, for I noticed how heavy 'twas; that new cashier gave me gold for most of it, you see."

"You'd have known then if you dropped it on the way, mother."

"I should think so: any way, I can't go to Boston without it! We may as well stop at the next station and go back."

So back they went; asked at the ticket office if any such thing had been picked up on the platform, and leaving a description of it, went rather forlornly back to the house. Here a terrible upturning of everything took place; drawers were emptied, cupboards ransacked, trunks explored, even the camphor chest examined to its depths, and everything in it shaken out.

"You don't suspect Mrs. Slack?" inquired Maria.

"Sally Slack! no, indeed. I've known her thirty year, Maria; she's honest as the daylight."

Still Maria thought it best to send for Mrs. Slack and inquire if she had seen it when she was at the house.

"Certain, certain!" answered the good woman. "I see Mis' Grant hev it into her hand when she went up charmber; I hedn't took no notice of it before, but she spoke up an' says, says she, 'I'll go right up now, Mis' Slack, for I'm in some of a hurry, bein' that I'm a goin' in the cars to Bosstown for to buy our folkses' Christmas things;' so then I took notice 't she hed a pocket-book into her hand."

This was valuable testimony, and Mrs. Slack's face of honest concern and sympathy showed her innocence in the matter. Next day there was an advertisement put in the paper, for the family concluded Grandma must have dropped her money in the street going to the station, but the advertisement proved as fruitless as the search, and for once in her life the dear old lady was downcast enough.

"The first time I never gave 'em a thing on Christmas! I do feel real downhearted about it, Maria. There's Annie's three girls lotted so on their gloves an' nicknacks for parties this winter, for I was goin' to give them gold pieces so's they could get what they wanted sort of fresh when they did want it; and poor Gerty's new cloak!"

"Oh, never mind that, mother. I can sponge and turn and fix over the old one; a plush collar and cuffs will make it all right."

"But there's the boys. Tom did want that set of tools and a bench for 'em; and I reckoned on seeing Harry's eyes shine over a real Newfoundland dog. That makes me think; won't you write to that man in New York? I've changed my mind about the dog. And Jack can't go to Thomas's now for vacation; oh dear!"

"Don't worry, mother," said Maria; but Grandma went on:

"Kate and Rosy too, they won't get their seal muffs and caps, and dear little Hal! how he will long for the books I promised him. It's real trying, Maria!" and Grandma wiped a tear from her eyes, a most unusual symptom.

But it was her way to make the best of things, and she sat down at once to tell Thomas of her loss, and then put it out of her mind as well as she might.

It spoke well for all those ten grandchildren that they each felt far more sorry for Grandmother Grant's disappointment than their own, and all resolved to give her a present much nicer and more expensive than ever before, pinching a little on their other gifts to the end; and because they had to spare from their own presents for this laudable purpose, it was natural enough that not one should tell another what they meant to send her, lest it should seem too extravagant in proportion to what the rest of the family received. Christmas morning the arrival began. The stocking of Grandpa's which Gerty had insisted on hanging to the knob of Grandma's door was full, and when she came down to breakfast she brought it with her still unsearched, that the family might enjoy her surprise.

At the top a square parcel tied with blue ribbon was marked "from Gerty," and proved to be a little velvet porte-monnaie.

"Dear child! how thoughtful!" said Grandma, giving her a kiss, and not observing that the doctor looked funnily at Mrs. White across the table.

The next package bore John's name and disclosed a pocket-book of Russia leather.

"So useful!" said Grandma, with a twinkle of gratitude in her kind old eyes.

Harry emitted a long low whistle, and his eyes shone as the next paper parcel with his name on it showed an honest black leather pocket-book with a steel clasp.

"Grandma had to laugh. Doctor White roared." Illustration by staff illustrator for *Wide Awake Magazine*, Vol. 16 No. 1 (December 1882).

Grandma had to laugh. Doctor White roared, and Tom looked a little rueful as his bundle produced another wallet as like to Harry's as two peas in a pod:

"Dear boys!" said Grandma, shaking like a liberal bowl of jelly with the laughter she tried to suppress in vain; but it was the boys' turn to shout as further explorations into the foot of the old blue stocking brought up a lovely seal-skin wallet from their mother, and a voluminous yellow leather one from the doctor.

> "Six souls with but a single thought;
>   Six hearts that beat as one;"

misquoted Mrs. Maria, and a chorus of laughter that almost rattled the windows followed her. They were still holding their sides and bursting out afresh every other minute, when little Sylvia Rutledge sailed into the dining-room with a delicate basket in her hand.

"Merry Christmas!" said she, "but you seem to have it already."

The boys all rushed at once to explain.

"Wait a minute," said she, "till I have given Grandma her gifts," and she produced successively from her basket four parcels.

Sylvia's held another velvet porte-monnaie; Annie's contained a second of hand-painted kid, daisies on a black ground; and Amelia's was a third pocket-book of gray canvas with Russia leather corners and straps; while Mrs. Rutledge's tiny packet produced an old-fashioned short purse, with steel fringe and clasp, which she had knit herself for her mother.

How can words tell the laughter which hailed this repetition?

The boys rolled off their chairs and roared till their very sides ached; tears streamed down Mrs. White's fair face; Grace gazed at the presents with a look half rueful and half funny, while the doctor's vigorous "haw! haw! haw!" could have been heard half a mile had it not been happily the season of shut doors and windows, while Sylvia herself perceiving the six pocket-books which had preceded her basketful, appreciated the situation and laughed all the harder because she was not tired with a previous fit of mirth, and Grandma sat shaking and chuckling in her chair, out of breath to be sure, but her face rosy and her eyes shining more than ever.

Suddenly a loud knock at the front door interrupted their laughter.

Tom ran to admit the intruder; it was the expressman with a box from New York directed in uncle Tom's hand to Mrs. J. G. Grant.

"Something better than pocket-books this time, mother!" said the doctor, as Tom ran for the screwdriver; but alas! the very first bundle that rolled out and fell heavily to the floor, proved when picked up to be indeed another pocket-book, cornered and clasped with silver, and Grandma's initials on the clasp; beautiful as the gift was it was thrust aside with a certain impatience, for the next package, labelled "from Rosamond," but opened only to display the very counterpart of Amelia's gift; and a paper box with Kate's script outside held the recurrent pocket-book again in black velvet and gilt corners, while a little carved white-wood box, the work of Hal's patient fingers, showed within its lid a purse of silvered links which had cost all his year's savings.

This was the last touch. Hitherto their curiosity as one thing was displayed after another had kept them in a sort of bubbling quiet, but this final development was too much; they laughed so loud and so long that old Hannah, hurrying from the kitchen and opening the door to see what was the matter, looked thunderstruck as she beheld the whole family shaking, choking, rolling about or holding on to each other in roars of sidesplitting laughter, while fourteen purses and pocket-books made the breakfast table look like a fancy fair.

"I thought I heard a crackling of thorns, as scripter says," she growled. "Be you a-going to set up a fancy store, Mis' White?"

"Bring in breakfast, Hannah," said the doctor, recovering himself.

"It's a melancholy truth that we can't eat pocket-books!"

For the satisfaction of the curious I must explain that the next May, when a certain old clock on the landing of the garret stairs was taken down to be put in order and made into a household god after the modern rage for such things, right under it lay Grandma's pocket-book intact.

"Well, now I remember!" said the astonished old lady, who never did remember where she had hidden anything till somebody else found it.

"I was goin' up to the chest to get out those things of husband's for Sally Slack, and I thought I wouldn't leave my pocket-book in my room, 'twould be putting temptation in her way, which isn't really right if a person is ever so honest; we're all frail as you may say when our time comes, and I didn't have my cloak on to put it in the pocket, and my under pocket was full, so I just slipped it under the clock case as I went up, feeling certain sure I should remember it because I never put it there before."

But the family voted that no harm had been done after all, for next Christmas the Rutledge girls each had a lovely silk party dress from the double fund; Gracie's cloak was mated by the prettiest hat and muff; Tom had his wild desire for a bicycle fulfilled; Harry owned a real gold watch which was far better than a dog; and Jack's ten gold eagles took him in the spring to Niagara and down the St. Lawrence, a journey never to be forgotten. Kate and Rosamond had their sealskin caps with muffs, gloves and velvet skirts to correspond with and supplement their last year's jackets; and Hal not only had his precious books, but a bookcase for them, and the pocket-books were redistributed among their givers; so that in the end good and not evil came of Grandma's losing her Christmas pocket-book!

Week Eleven:

COLORADO SNOW-BIRDS

I'll tell you how the snow-birds come,
    Here in our Winter days;
They make me think of chickens,
    With their cunning little ways.

We go to bed at night, and leave
    The ground all bare and brown,
And not a single snow-bird
    To be seen in all the town.

But when we wake at morning
    The ground with snow is white,
And with the snow, the snow-birds
    Must have travelled all the night;

For the streets and yards are full of them,
    The dainty little things,
With snow-white breasts, and soft brown heads,
    And speckled russet wings.

Not here and there a snow-bird,
    As we see them at the East,
But in great flocks, like grasshoppers,
    By hundreds, at the least,

They push and crowd and jostle,
    And twitter as they feed,
And hardly lift their heads up,
    For fear to miss a seed.

What 'tis they eat, nobody seems
    To know or understand;
The seeds are much too fine to see,
    All sifted in the sand.

But winds last Summer scattered them,
    All thickly on these plains;
The little snow-birds have no barns,
    But God protects their grains.

They let us come quite near them,
    And show no sign of dread;
Then in a twinkling, the whole flock
    Will flutter on ahead

A step or two, and light, and feed,
    And look demure and tame,
And then fly on again, and stop,
    As if it were a game.

Some flocks count up to thousands,
    I know, and when they fly,
Their tiny wings make rustle
    As if a wind went by.

They go as quickly as they come,
    Go in a night or day;
Soon as the snow has melted off,
    The darlings fly away,

But come again, again, again,
    All Winter, with each snow;
Brave little armies, through the cold;
    Swift back and forth they go.

I always wondered where they lived
    In Summer, till last year
I stumbled on them in their home,
    High in the upper air;

'Way up among the clouds it was,
    A many thousand feet,
But on the mountain-side gay flowers
    Were blooming fresh and sweet.

Great pine-trees' swaying branches
    Gave cool and fragrant shade;
And here, we found, the snow-birds
    Their Summer home had made.

"Oh, lucky little snow-birds!"
    We said, "to know so well,
In Summer time and Winter time,
    Your destined place to dwell—

"To journey, nothing doubting,
    Down to the barren plains,
Where harvests are all over,
    To find your garnered grains!

"Oh, precious little snow-birds!
    If we were half as wise,
If we were half as trusting
    To the Father in the skies,—

"He would feed us, though the harvests
   Had ceased throughout the land,
And hold us, all our lifetime,
   In the hollow of his hand!"
                    HELEN HUNT JACKSON
                        (1830–1885)

Week Twelve:

CHRISTMAS AT RED BUTTE

Canadian Short Story

BY LUCY MAUD MONTGOMERY

"Of course Santa Claus will come," said Jimmy Martin confidently. Jimmy was ten, and at ten it is easy to be confident. "Why, he's got to come because it is Christmas Eve, and he always has come. You know that, twins."

Yes, the twins knew it and, cheered by Jimmy's superior wisdom, their doubts passed away. There had been one terrible moment when Theodora had sighed and told them they mustn't be too much disappointed if Santa Claus did not come this year because the crops had been poor, and he mightn't have had enough presents to go around.

"That doesn't make any difference to Santa Claus," scoffed Jimmy. "You know as well as I do, Theodora Prentice, that Santa Claus is rich whether the crops fail or not. They failed three years ago, before Father died, but Santa Claus came all the same. Prob'bly you don't remember it, twins, 'cause you were too little, but I do. Of course he'll come, so don't you worry a mite. And he'll bring my skates and your dolls. He knows we're expecting them, Theodora, 'cause we wrote him a letter last week, and threw it up the chimney. And there'll be candy and nuts, of course, and Mother's gone to town to buy a turkey. I tell you we're going to have a ripping Christmas."

"Well, don't use such slangy words about it, Jimmy-boy," sighed Theodora. She couldn't bear to dampen their hopes any further, and perhaps Aunt Elizabeth might manage it if the colt sold well. But

Theodora had her painful doubts, and she sighed again as she looked out of the window far down the trail that wound across the prairie, red-lighted by the declining sun of the short wintry afternoon.

"Do people always sigh like that when they get to be sixteen?" asked Jimmy curiously. "You didn't sigh like that when you were only fifteen, Theodora. I wish you wouldn't. It makes me feel funny—and it's not a nice kind of funniness either."

"It's a bad habit I've got into lately," said Theodora, trying to laugh. "Old folks are dull sometimes, you know, Jimmy-boy."

"Sixteen is awful old, isn't it?" said Jimmy reflectively. "I'll tell you what I'm going to do when I'm sixteen, Theodora. I'm going to pay off the mortgage, and buy mother a silk dress, and a piano for the twins. Won't that be elegant? I'll be able to do that 'cause I'm a man. Of course if I was only a girl I couldn't."

"I hope you'll be a good kind brave man and a real help to your mother," said Theodora softly, sitting down before the cosy fire and lifting the fat little twins into her lap.

"Oh, I'll be good to her, never you fear," assured Jimmy, squatting comfortably down on the little fur rug before the stove—the skin of the coyote his father had killed four years ago. "I believe in being good to your mother when you've only got the one. Now tell us a story, Theodora—a real jolly story, you know, with lots of fighting in it. Only please don't kill anybody. I like to hear about fighting, but I like to have all the people come out alive."

Theodora laughed, and began a story about the Riel Rebellion of '85—a story which had the double merit of being true and exciting at the same time. It was quite dark when she finished, and the twins were nodding, but Jimmy's eyes were wide open and sparkling.

"That was great," he said, drawing a long breath. "Tell us another."

"No, it's bedtime for you all," said Theodora firmly. "One story at a time is my rule, you know."

"But I want to sit up till Mother comes home," objected Jimmy.

"You can't. She may be very late, for she would have to wait to see Mr. Porter. Besides, you don't know what time Santa Claus might come—if he comes at all. If he were to drive along and see you children up instead of being sound asleep in bed, he might go right on and never call at all."

This argument was too much for Jimmy.

"All right, we'll go. But we have to hang up our stockings first. Twins, get yours."

The twins toddled off in great excitement, and brought back their Sunday stockings, which Jimmy proceeded to hang along the edge of the mantel shelf. This done, they all trooped obediently off to bed. Theodora gave another sigh, and seated herself at the window, where she could watch the moonlit prairie for Mrs. Martin's homecoming and knit at the same time.

I am afraid that you will think from all the sighing Theodora was doing that she was a very melancholy and despondent young lady. You couldn't think anything more unlike the real Theodora. She was the jolliest, bravest girl of sixteen in all Saskatchewan, as her shining brown eyes and rosy, dimpled cheeks would have told you; and her sighs were not on her own account, but simply for fear the children were going to be disappointed. She knew that they would be almost heartbroken if Santa Claus did not come, and that this would hurt the patient hardworking little mother more than all else.

Five years before this, Theodora had come to live with Uncle George and Aunt Elizabeth in the little log house at Red Butte. Her own mother had just died, and Theodora had only her big brother Donald left, and Donald had Klondike fever. The Martins were poor, but they had gladly made room for their little niece, and Theodora had lived there ever since, her aunt's right-hand girl and the beloved playmate of the children. They had been very happy until Uncle George's death two years before this Christmas Eve; but since then there had been hard times in the little log house, and though Mrs. Martin and Theodora did their best, it was a woefully hard task to make both ends meet, especially this year when their crops had been poor. Theodora and her aunt had made every sacrifice possible for the children's sake, and at least Jimmy and the twins had not felt the pinch very severely yet.

At seven Mrs. Martin's bells jingled at the door and Theodora flew out. "Go right in and get warm, Auntie," she said briskly. "I'll take Ned away and unharness him."

"It's a bitterly cold night," said Mrs. Martin wearily. There was a note of discouragement in her voice that struck dismay to Theodora's heart.

"I'm afraid it means no Christmas for the children tomorrow," she thought sadly, as she led Ned away to the stable. When she returned to the kitchen Mrs. Martin was sitting by the fire, her face in her chilled hand, sobbing convulsively.

"Auntie—oh, Auntie, don't!" exclaimed Theodora impulsively. It was such a rare thing to see her plucky, resolute little aunt in tears. "You're cold and tired—I'll have a nice cup of tea for you in a trice."

"No, it isn't that," said Mrs. Martin brokenly. "It was seeing those stockings hanging there. Theodora, I couldn't get a thing for the children—not a single thing. Mr. Porter would only give forty dollars for the colt, and when all the bills were paid there was barely enough left for such necessaries as we must have. I suppose I ought to feel thankful I could get those. But the thought of the children's disappointment tomorrow is more than I can bear. It would have been better to have told them long ago, but I kept building on getting more for the colt. Well, it's weak and foolish to give way like this. We'd better both take a cup of tea and go to bed. It will save fuel."

When Theodora went up to her little room her face was very thoughtful. She took a small box from her table and carried it to the window. In it was a very pretty little gold locket hung on a narrow blue ribbon. Theodora held it tenderly in her fingers, and looked out over the moonlit prairie with a very sober face. Could she give up her dear locket—the locket Donald had given her just before he started for the Klondike? She had never thought she could do such a thing. It was almost the only thing she had to remind her of Donald—handsome, merry, impulsive, warmhearted Donald, who had gone away four years ago with a smile on his bonny face and splendid hope in his heart.

"Here's a locket for you, Gift o' God," he had said gaily—he had such a dear loving habit of calling her by the beautiful meaning of her name. A lump came into Theodora's throat as she remembered it. "I couldn't afford a chain too, but when I come back I'll bring you a rope of Klondike nuggets for it."

Then he had gone away. For two years letters had come from him regularly. Then he wrote that he had joined a prospecting party to a remote wilderness. After that was silence, deepening into anguish of suspense that finally ended in hopelessness. A rumour came that Donald Prentice was dead. None had returned from the expedition he had joined. Theodora had long ago given up all hope of ever seeing Donald again. Hence her locket was doubly dear to her.

But Aunt Elizabeth had always been so good and loving and kind to her. Could she not make the sacrifice for her sake? Yes, she could and would. Theodora flung up her head with a gesture that meant decision. She took out of the locket the bits of hair—her mother's and Donald's—which it contained (perhaps a tear or two fell as she did so) and then hastily donned her warmest cap and wraps. It was only three miles to Spencer; she could easily walk it in an hour and, as it was Christmas Eve, the shops would be open late. She [must] walk, for Ned could not be taken out again, and the mare's foot was sore. Besides, Aunt Elizabeth must not know until it was done.

As stealthily as if she were bound on some nefarious errand, Theodora slipped downstairs and out of the house. The next minute she was hurrying along the trail in the moonlight. The great dazzling prairie was around her, the mystery and splendour of the northern night all about her. It was very calm and cold, but Theodora walked so briskly that she kept warm. The trail from Red Butte to Spencer was a lonely one. Mr. Lurgan's house, halfway to town, was the only dwelling on it.

When Theodora reached Spencer she made her way at once to the only jewellery store the little town contained. Mr. Benson, its owner, had been a friend of her uncle's, and Theodora felt sure that he would buy her locket. Nevertheless her heart beat quickly, and her breath came and went uncomfortably fast as she went in. Suppose he wouldn't buy it. Then there would be no Christmas for the children at Red Butte.

"Good evening, Miss Theodora," said Mr. Benson briskly. "What can I do for you?"

"I'm afraid I'm not a very welcome sort of customer, Mr. Benson," said Theodora, with an uncertain smile. "I want to sell, not buy. Could you—will you buy this locket?"

Mr. Benson pursed up his lips, took up the locket, and examined it. "Well, I don't often buy second-hand stuff," he said, after some reflection, "but I don't mind obliging you, Miss Theodora. I'll give you four dollars for this trinket."

Theodora knew the locket had cost a great deal more than that, but four dollars would get what she wanted, and she dared not ask for more. In a few minutes the locket was in Mr. Benson's possession, and Theodora, with four crisp new bills in her purse, was hurrying to the toy store. Half an hour later she was on her way back to Red Butte, with as many parcels as she could carry—Jimmy's skates, two lovely dolls for the twins, packages of nuts and candy, and a nice plump turkey. Theodora beguiled her lonely tramp by picturing the children's joy in the morning.

About a quarter of a mile past Mr. Lurgan's house the trail curved suddenly about a bluff of poplars. As Theodora rounded the turn she halted in amazement. Almost at her feet the body of a man was lying across the road. He was clad in a big fur coat, and had a fur cap pulled well down over his forehead and ears. Almost all of him that could be seen was a full bushy beard. Theodora had no idea who he was, or where he had come from. But she realized that he was unconscious, and that he would speedily freeze to death if help were not brought. The footprints of a horse galloping across the prairie suggested a fall and a runaway, but Theodora did not waste time in speculation. She ran back at full speed to Mr. Lurgan's, and roused the household. In a few minutes Mr. Lurgan and his son had hitched a horse to a wood-sleigh, and hurried down the trail to the unfortunate man.

Theodora, knowing that her assistance was not needed, and that she ought to get home as quickly as possible, went on her way as soon as she had seen the stranger in safe keeping. When she reached the little log house she crept in, cautiously put the children's gifts in their stockings, placed the turkey on the table where Aunt Elizabeth would see it the first thing in the morning, and then slipped off to bed, a very weary but very happy girl.

The joy that reigned in the little log house the next day more than repaid Theodora for her sacrifice.

"Whoopee, didn't I tell you that Santa Claus would come all right!" shouted the delighted Jimmy. "Oh, what splendid skates!"

The twins hugged their dolls in silent rapture, but Aunt Elizabeth's face was the best of all.

Then the dinner had to be prepared, and everybody had a hand in that. Just as Theodora, after a grave peep into the oven, had announced that the turkey was done, a sleigh dashed around the house. Theodora flew to answer the knock at the door, and there stood Mr. Lurgan and a big, bewhiskered, fur-coated fellow whom Theodora recognized as the stranger she had found on the trail. But—was he a stranger? There was something oddly familiar in those merry brown eyes. Theodora felt herself growing dizzy.

"Donald!" she gasped. "Oh, Donald!"

And then she was in the big fellow's arms, laughing and crying at the same time.

Donald it was indeed. And then followed half an hour during which everybody talked at once, and the turkey would have been burned to a crisp had it not been for the presence of mind of Mr. Lurgan who, being the least excited of them all, took it out of the oven, and set it on the back of the stove.

"To think that it was you last night, and that I never dreamed it," exclaimed Theodora. "Oh, Donald, if I hadn't gone to town!"

"I'd have frozen to death, I'm afraid," said Donald soberly. "I got into Spencer on the last train last night. I felt that I must come right out—I couldn't wait till morning. But there wasn't a team to be got for love or money—it was Christmas Eve and all the livery rigs were out. So I came on horseback. Just by that bluff something frightened my horse, and he shied violently. I was half asleep and thinking of my little sister, and I went off like a shot. I suppose I struck my head against a tree. Anyway, I knew nothing more until I came to in Mr. Lurgan's kitchen. I wasn't much hurt—feel none the worse of it except for a sore head and shoulder. But, oh, Gift o' God, how you have grown! I can't realize that you are the little sister I left four years ago. I suppose you have been thinking I was dead?"

"Yes, and, oh, Donald, where have you been?"

"Well, I went way up north with a prospecting party. We had a tough time the first year, I can tell you, and some of us never came back. We weren't in a country where post offices were lying round loose either, you see. Then at last, just as we were about giving up in despair, we struck it rich. I've brought a snug little pile home with me, and things are going to look up in this log house, Gift o' God. There'll be no more worrying for you dear people over mortgages."

"I'm so glad—for Auntie's sake," said Theodora, with shining eyes. "But, oh, Donald, it's best of all just to have you back. I'm so perfectly happy that I don't know what to do or say."

"Well, I think you might have dinner," said Jimmy in an injured tone. "The turkey's getting stone cold, and I'm most starving. I just can't stand it another minute."

So, with a laugh, they all sat down to the table and ate the merriest Christmas dinner the little log house had ever known.

Week Twelve:

A Visit from St. Nicholas

'Twas the night before Christmas, when all through the house
    Not a creature was stirring, not even a mouse;
The stockings were hung by the chimney with care,
    In hopes that St. Nicholas soon would be there;

The children were nestled all snug in their beds,
    While visions of sugar-plums danced in their heads;
And mamma in her kerchief, and I in my cap,
    Had just settled our brains for a long winter's nap—

When out on the lawn there rose such a clatter,
    I sprang from my bed to see what was the matter,
Away to the window I flew like a flash,
    Tore open the shutters and threw up the sash.

The moon, on the breast of the new-fallen snow,
  Gave a lustre of mid-day to objects below;
When, what to my wondering eyes should appear,
  But a miniature sleigh, and eight tiny rein-deer,

With a little old driver, so lively and quick,
  I knew in a moment it must be St. Nick.
More rapid than eagles his coursers they came,
  And he whistled, and shouted, and called them by name;

"Now, Dasher! now, Dancer! now, Prancer and Vixen!
  On! Comet, on! Cupid, on! Donder and Blitzen—
To the top of the porch, to the top of the wall!
  Now, dash away, dash away, dash away all!"

As dry leaves that before the wild hurricane fly,
  When they meet with an obstacle, mount to the sky,
So, up to the house-top the coursers they flew,
  With a sleigh full of toys—and St. Nicholas too.

And then in a twinkling I heard on the roof,
  The prancing and pawing of each little hoof.
As I drew in my head, and was turning around,
  Down the chimney St. Nicholas came with a bound.

He was dressed all in fur from his head to his foot,
  And his clothes were all tarnished with ashes and soot;
A bundle of toys he had flung on his back,
  And he looked like a peddler just opening his pack;

His eyes how they twinkled! his dimples how merry!
  His cheeks were like roses, his nose like a cherry;
His droll little mouth was drawn up like a bow,
  And the beard on his chin was as white as the snow;

The stump of a pipe he held tight in his teeth,
  And the smoke, it encircled his head like a wreath.
He had a broad face, and a little round belly
  That shook when he laughed, like a bowl full of jelly.

He was chubby and plump—a right jolly old elf;
  And I laughed when I saw him in spite of myself.
A wink of his eye, and a twist of his head,
  Soon gave me to know I had nothing to dread.

All illustrations for this poem are by Jessie Willcox Smith in *'Twas the Night Before Christmas: A Visit from Saint Nicholas* by Clement C. Moore (Boston and New York: Houghton Mifflin Co., 1912).

He spoke not a word, but went straight to his work,
  And filled all the stockings; then turned with a jerk,
And laying his finger aside of his nose,
  And giving a nod, up the chimney he rose.

He sprang to his sleigh, to his team gave a whistle,
  And away they all flew like the down of a thistle;
But I heard him exclaim, ere he drove out of sight,
  "Merry Christmas to all, and to all a good night!"
CLEMENT CLARKE MOORE
(1779–1863)

Week Thirteen:

CROCKETT'S FIGHT WITH A CATFISH

American Tall Tale

BY DAVY CROCKETT

There is one of my young scrapes that has never yet appeared in print, and I think I might as well give it to the reader in this place.

I cut out one morning to go over the Mississippi on business that concerns nobody but myself. I shoved off my canoe and had paddled into the middle of the stream, when a monstratious great Cat-Fish, better known by the name of a Mississippi Lawyer, came swimming along close under the bows of my boat. I tied a rope around my middle, at one end of it was a fishing spear, and I soon got a chance to dart it into the varmint. He ran and I hauled, and it whirled my canoe round and round like a car-wheel on a railroad. I concluded to stand up to my rack, and I couldn't very well help it, seeing that one end of the rope was made fast to my middle. At last on account of his giving one end of the line a tremendous kick with his tail, and partly on account of the canoe slipping away from under me, I went souse into the water. The cat-fish at the same time seized the slack of my breeches with his teeth and tore them clear off me. I didn't care much for that, as it was easier swimming without them. So I drew out my knife, and when the fish came up and made a pass at my throat with his open mouth, I stabbed out one of his eyes. That made him plunge, but as he was going down I grabbed him by the tail, and went down with him till I touched bottom with one foot. All this lime the spear remained in the plaguy varmint, and while under water, I come across a sawyer that was sticking up; I took a turn with my line around this sawyer, and the fish was brought up all standing. So he come at me again, and I manœuvred to get on the blind side of him—but he could see better under water than I could, though he had but one eye left, and he turned short upon me just as I was about stabbing him to the heart. I then clinched right round his body, and rammed one arm down his throat, while I tried to stab him with the other hand—then I tell you the fire flew. I never see a fellow kick, bite and scratch as he did. I had been under water a pretty good long while, and there was a ringing in my ears that warned me to finish my job as soon as I could. "I tell you there's no quarter to be given," said I to the fish, perceiving him to grow a little faintish. With that he fell to fighting again, and I believe he would have scratched my bones bare, if I had not got a chance to shove my knife to the hilt in his belly. I then cut my line, and rose to the surface pretty well fagged out. Arter I had rested a spell, I dove down and tied a line to the fish and pulled up his corpse. It measured twelve feet in length.

Week Thirteen:

The Heroine of Kaintuck

American Tall Tale

by Davy Crockett

Of all the ripsnorters I ever tutched upon, thar never war one that could pull her boat alongside of Grace Peabody, the horowine of Kaintuck. When she got her temper fairly up, she war more like seven thunder bolts, withed together with chain litening, than a human cretur. Her father war a squatter; but she ganed a residence as she war born in the plaice. I reckon that all the varmints in the state stood in fear of her, and would sooner stick their tales in a steal trap, than feel the gripe of her thum and 4 finger around their throttles. She had a most abstemious eye, and when she gave one look at a painter or a bear, he thought the sun had riz within rifle shot of his nose. She minded no sort of weather. She would go through a snow-bank without looking for the path, and would shed rain like a duck. It took seven women to hold her when she sneezed, and they said that when she was insulted by a Tennessee bully in the month of March, she jumped clean out of her close, she war so furce to cum at him. She cum pretty neer gitting discharged one onlucky morning in September. She war going to carry home some work, for she got her living by making Prarie pillows, which war bear-skins stuffed with buffalo horn scrapings, and they war made for two conveniences, to sleep on for one, and for the tother, when your head itched in the nite, you could skratch it by rubbing it agin the piller. So she did her arrant, and then sot out to cum home through the woods, as it war gitting late in the arternoon.

She hadn't got fur before she perseeved she was follored by something of the four-legged kind. She war not skared at all, and it would be a dangerous predicament for the bridge of a man's knows, who should tell her she war ever skared at enny thing. But she kepp one korner of her eye open, and wawked on. In a little while she kinder thort she saw about fifty wolves coming around her and jumping at her throat. As she coodent kill 'em all at once, she run up a tree that grew slanting, and when she got to the top of it she begun to break off pieces of the limbs and throw at 'em; and she killed two or three of the pesky creturs in this way; and made one of 'em gape for fourteen sekonds, as she hit him between the two ize with a twig as big round as her leg. But jist as she was killing them off by degrees, a bear cum up out of the tree, which war holler inside, and he bolted out so quick that he took her with him, and they cum doun together on the ground; but Grace hung on upon the bear and cum down astraddle of his back. The wolves got out of the way when they cum down, like when you throw a stone in the water; but they closed up as the bear begun to run. Grace had a bit of stick in her hand, about as long as my rifle, and as thick at one eend as a cat's body. The bear didn't like to have a rider, and the wolves tride to help him git her off; and as he cut through the dry leaves, with the wolves all around him, jumping at Grace, the leaves and twigs flew about, so that you couldn't see nothing but Grace's cudgel as she swung it over her head, to bring it down upon the profile of some infarnul wolf, that was left rolling in the forrest behind them, and spouting the bloody foam from his lips. But the wolves cum thicker and thicker, and Grace begun to git tired in the arms. She held on upon the bear's wool as well as she could; but he run and jumped and roared, bekase he knew it was all Grace's fault that the wolves rained around him like a snow-storm. Grace's cudgel begun to splinter, and the pesky varmints took advantage of that sarcumstance, for ther is no onor about 'em, and they care no more for fare play than an injun kares for the sarmont on the mountin. Grace begun to think her time had cum, for one wolf had tore off the soul of her shew, and another one had got the skirt of her gownd in his teeth. She was jist about letting go of the bear and dropping down among the wolves, when help cum. I had been out that arternoon with Grizzle a-hunting. Grizzle told me as plane as he cood speak, that thar war something to pay in the bushes, and I run down that way; and sure enuff, I seed the twigs and leeves a-flying like thar war a small arth-quake running along the ground. In a minnit the bear cum bolting out from a thicket, with wolves all around him, and I seed the cudgel agoing, but couldn't see Grace till I got close to her. I pulled trigger upon the varmints, and shot two. Then Grizzle and I went in among 'em like the wonderful workings of Providence in a thunder storm, and the wolves scattered jist as Grace cum to the ground. The bear got off cleer, for I sposed he had done good sarviss, and tis not the fashun with Davy Crockett to do an ongrateful axeshun. Grace told me I had saved her life, and a fortnite from that day, she sent me a pair of new stockings that she had gnit out of wolf-sinues.

Spring Frost (detail) by Elioth Gruner (1919). Art Gallery of New South Wales.

Week Thirteen:
THE FROST

The Frost looked forth one still, clear night,
And whispered, "Now I shall be out of sight;
So through the valley and over the height,
　　In silence I'll take my way.
I will not go on like that blustering train,
The wind and the snow, the hail and the rain,
Who make so much bustle and noise in vain,
　　But I'll be as busy as they!"

Then he flew to the mountain, and powdered its crest;
He lit on the trees, and their boughs he drest
In diamond beads—and over the breast
　　Of the quivering lake, he spread
A coat of mail, that it need not fear
The downward point of many a spear,
That he hung on its margin, far and near,
　　Where a rock could rear its head.

He went to the windows of those who slept,
And over each pane, like a fairy, crept;
Wherever he breathed, wherever he stepped,
   By the light of the morn were seen
Most beautiful things; there were flowers and trees;
There were bevies of birds and swarms of bees;
There were cities with temples and towers; and these
   All pictured in silver sheen!

But he did one thing that was hardly fair—
He peeped in the cupboard, and finding there
That all had forgotten for him to prepare,
   "Now, just to set them a-thinking,
I'll bite this basket of fruit," said he,
"This costly pitcher I'll burst in three;
And the glass of water they've left for me
   Shall 'tchick!' to tell them I'm drinking!"
               HANNAH FLAGG GOULD
                  (1789–1865)

Week Fourteen:

MRS. CUTTLE AND THE CATAMOUNT

American Tall Tale

BY DAVY CROCKETT

One day I fell in with Jo Cuttle. Jo war an honest ruff-and tumble sort of chap, and arter we had jogged on a little way, sez he, "Kurnel, thar war a pesky queer scrape onct happened to me in these diggins. It war arter this sort:

"It war late one arternoon when my wife war cuming home from a tea-squall. She war passing rite thro' the forrest, and had forgot to bring her rifle with her. But she never war afeard of any thing less than a bull mammoth, and so she jogged along as merry and contented as a she bear. She cum to a deep hollow whar war a large pond of water, and she saw a big log lying near, and she rolled it in. As soon as the log war afloat, she got on one end of it with her face towards the opposite shore, and begun to paddle across. When she got about haff way over, she happened to hear a low growl, and when she looked behind she saw that a great catamount sot on the other end of the log. He had took passage with her when she fust started, but she did not see him then. As my wife war sitting straddle, it took sum time for her to turn round, and face the catamount. He showed his teeth and grouled because she had left off paddling; so she concluded that he meant to behave civil, if she wood only carry him safe across; but she had an idee that arter they war fairly landed, he would try to make a breakfast of her. So she would not paddle another stroke. He kept growling, as much as to say, 'Row

"Mrs. Cuttle and the Catamount." Illustration by John H. Manning in *The Crockett Almanac*, Vol. 2, No. 3 (Nashville, TN: Ben Harding, 1841).

away you infarnal jade!' That made her mad, for she cood understand his language jist as well as if she had been born to it; so she dashed water on him with her paddle. This made him wink a little, and he showed his teeth. When she seed he war going to spring rite at her, she jist canted the log and he tumbled into the drink, but he put his paws up to get hold of the log agin, and kept trying to gain a foothold on it,

which kept it turning round and round like a grindstone, till my wife's legs war chafed most ridiculous. At last she found she must get upon her feet, and then she war forced to keep hopping up and down all the time—she danced while the catamount fiddled upon the log.—She then stomped on his paws, but he minded no more about that than a flea bite. So she watched a chance and gave a jump rite on the feller's back, and caught hold of both of his ears. When ever he tried to bite her, she wood bowse his head under and haff drown him. Then he set out to swim for the shore, and she kept upon his back, and guided him by pulling his right or left ear, jist as she wanted he shood go. Well, he got safe ashore with her, and she didn't dare let go of his ears, or to get off for fear he wood be into her like a buck-shot.

"Now I happened to be out hunting, with one Kit Weatherow at this time, and Kit cum running to me, and told me he saw the strangest cretur going through the woods that he ever seed in his life before. He said it war a wild varmint in petticoats. I told Kit to go with me to hunt it up, for I had seen every cretur in the forrest, and this must be a stranger. We soon cum in sight of it, but I new my wife's petticoat as soon as I got a glimpse at it, and then I seed her head a little while arterward. So sez I to Kit, sing dumb, and let me get a blizzard at the obstropolous varmint, for he's running off with my wife. I lifted my rifle and put a hole rite through his gizzard: but I shot away one of my wife's cap-strings at the same time, which war made of buffalo sinew. The varmint tumbled amongst the leaves pretty quick, and my wife picked herself off the ground in less than no time. When I seed she want hurt, I felt a little mad, and told her never agin to clasp around the neck of any living thing but her own lawful husband."

Week Fourteen:
KATY GOODGRIT
AND THE WOLVES
American Tall Tale
BY DAVY CROCKETT

Katy Goodgrit war a favorite of mine, bekase when her spunk war up, she could grin a wildcat out of countenance, and make a streak of lightning back out. She didn't care for anything that went on four legs, nor anything that went on two legs. One day she war going out into the woods, and seed two wolves shying along like a snake in the grass, not a great ways off; and she intarmined to put a stop to 'em, for they looked very obnoxious, and seemed to want to be tasting sumthing of the human kind. So she took up a club, and walked in between 'em. They begun to feel amazing skittish when they seed her coming with the club, but at last they come towards her. She gave one of 'em a monstracious tap on the head with her club, and he squawked right out. Before she had time to hit the other, she heerd a pattering amongst the leaves, and when she lookt around, thar war about fifty wolves coming towards her on the full trot.

Some gals would have ben skeered out of thar seven wits, but Katy always knowed it war the fust duty of a gal of Kaintuck to stand up to her lick log, salt or no salt. So she just squatted low for the present, and got up into a holler stump whar the wolves couldn't quite reach her, and they come roaring around her, like the water boiling around Crocodile Rock, at Tumble Down Falls. They jumpt up even most to her face, and she spit at one so violent that it knocked his eye out. She cotch another by the scurf of his neck, and whipt his head off agin the tree. So she kept stopping their wind, till the fust she knew thar war a pile of dead wolves around the tree, high enough for the others to climb up on it. Then she war obleeged to squat down, or they would have tore her head off.

She staid thar all nite; but early the nixt morning she stuck up her head, and crowed, till she crowed and screamed all the wolves deaf, and then they begun to clear out, but she went arter 'em with a pole and killed half of 'em before they got away.

Week Fourteen:

HOME, SWEET HOME

Mid pleasures and palaces though we may roam,
Be it ever so humble, there's no place like home.
A charm from the skies seems to hallow us there,
Which, seek through the world, is ne'er met with elsewhere.

Home! home! sweet, sweet home!
There's no place like home!
There's no place like home!

An exile from home, splendor dazzles in vain;
Oh! give me my lowly thatch'd cottage again!
The birds singing gaily, that come at my call,
Give me them, with the peace of mind, dearer than all.

Home! home! sweet, sweet home!
There's no place like home!
There's no place like home!

"The cares of a mother to soothe and beguile" and other illustrations with this poem by Miss L. B. Humphrey for John Howard Payne in "Home, Sweet Home" (Boston, John Andrew & Son. 1880).

How sweet 'tis to sit 'neath a fond father's smile,
And the cares of a mother to soothe and beguile!
Let others delight 'mid new pleasures to roam,
But give, oh! give me the pleasures of home!

Home! home! sweet, sweet home!
But give me, oh! give me,
The pleasures of home.

To thee I'll return, overburdened with care:
The heart's dearest solace will smile on me there.
No more from that cottage again will I roam:
Be it ever so humble, there's no place like home.

Home! home! sweet, sweet home!
There's no place like home!
There's no place like home!

To us, in spite of the absence of years,
How sweet the remembrance of home still appears!
From allurements abroad, which but flatter the eye,
The unsatisfied heart turns, and says, with a sigh:

"Home! home! sweet, sweet home!
There's no place like home!
There's no place like home!"

Your exile is blest with all fate can bestow,
But mine has been checkered with many a woe;
Yet, though different our fortunes, our thoughts are the same,
And both, as we think of Columbia, exclaim:

"Home! home! sweet, sweet home!
There's no place like home!
There's no place like home!"
                    JOHN HOWARD PAYNE
                        (1791–1852)

"Pecos Bill." Illustration by Elmer Hader for *The New Century Illustrated Monthly Magazine*, Vol. 106 No. 6 (October 1923).

Week Fifteen:
The Saga of Pecos Bill
American Tall Tale
by Edward O'Reilly

Bill invented most of the things connected with the cow business. He was a mighty man of valor, the king killer of the bad men, and it was Bill who taught the broncho how to buck. It is a matter of record that he dug the Rio Grande one dry year when he grew tired of packin' water from the Gulf of Mexico.

According to the most veracious historians, Bill was born about the time Sam Houston discovered Texas. He cut his teeth on a bowie-knife, and his earliest playfellows were the bears and catamounts of east Texas.

When Bill was about a year old, another family moved into the country, and located about fifty miles down the river. His father decided the place was gettin' too crowded, and packed his family in a wagon and headed west.

One day after they crossed the Pecos River, Bill fell out of the wagon. As there were sixteen or seventeen other children in the family, his parents didn't miss him for four or five weeks, and then it was too late to try to find him.

That's how Bill came to grow up with the coyotes along the Pecos. He soon learned the coyote language, and used to hunt with them and sit on the hills and howl at night. Being so young when he got lost, he always thought he was a coyote. That's where he learned to kill deer by runnin' them to death.

One day when he was about ten years old a cow-boy came along just when Bill had matched a fight with two grizzly bears. Bill hugged the bears to death, tore off a hind leg, and was just settin' down to breakfast when this cow-boy loped up and asked him what he meant by runnin' around naked that way among the varmints. "Why, because I am a varmint," Bill told him. "I'm a coyote." The cow-boy argued with him that he was a human, but Bill wouldn't believe him.

"Ain't I got fleas?" he insisted. "And don't I howl around all night, like a respectable coyote should do?" "That don't prove nothin'," the cow-boy answered. "All Texans have fleas, and most of them howl. Did you ever see a coyote that didn't have a tail? Well, you ain't got no tail; so that proves you ain't a varmint."

Bill looked, and, sure enough, he didn't have a tail.

"You sure' got me out on a limb," says Bill. "I never noticed that before. It shows what higher education will do for a man. I believe you're right. Lead me to them humans, and I'll throw in with them."

Bill went to town with this cow-hand, and in due time he got to enjoyin' all the pleasant vices of mankind, and decided that he certainly was a human. He got to runnin' with the wild bunch, and sunk lower and lower, until finally he became a cow-boy.

He saddled up his horse and hit for the West. One day he met an old trapper and told him what he was lookin' for.

"I want the hardest cow outfit in the world," he says.

"Stranger, you're headed in the right direction," answers the trapper. "Keep right on down this draw for a couple of hundred miles, and you 'll find that very outfit. They're so hard they can kick fire out of a flint rock with their bare toes."

Bill single-footed down that draw for about a hundred miles that afternoon; then he met with an accident.

His horse stubbed his toe on a mountain and broke his leg, leavin' Bill afoot.

All at once a big ten-foot rattle snake quiled up in his path, set his tail to singin', and allowed he'd like to match a fight. Bill laid down his saddle, and just to be fair about it, he gave the snake the first three bites.

Then he waded into that reptile and everlastingly frailed the pizen out of him.

By and by that old rattler yelled for mercy, and admitted that when it came to fightin', Bill started where he left off. So Bill picked up his saddle and started on, carryin' the snake in his hand and spinnin' it in short loops at the Gila monsters.

About fifty miles further on, a big old mountain-lion jumped off a cliff and lit all spraddled out on Bill's neck. This was no ordinary lion. It weighed more than three steers and a yearlin', and was the very same lion the State of Nuevo León was named after down in old Mexico.

Kind of chucklin' to himself, Bill laid down his saddle and his snake and went into action. In a minute the fur was flyin' down the cañon until it darkened the sun. The way Bill knocked the animosity out of that lion was a shame. In about three minutes that lion hollered:

"I'll give up, Bill. Can't you take a joke?"

Bill let him up, and then he cinched the saddle on him and went down that cañon whoopin' and yellin', ridin' that lion a hundred feet at a jump, and quirtin' him down the flank with the rattlesnake.

It wasn't long before he saw a chuck-wagon, with a bunch of cow-boys squattin' around it. He rode up to that wagon, splittin' the air with his war-whoops, with that old lion a screechin', and that snake singin' his rattles.

When he came to the fire he grabbed the old cougar by the ear, jerked him back on his haunches, stepped off him, hung his snake around his neck, and looked the outfit over. Them cow-boys sat there sayin' less than nothin'. Bill was hungry, and seein' a boilerful of beans cookin' on the fire, he scooped up a few handfuls and swallowed them, washin' them down with a few gallons of boilin' coffee out of the pot. Wipin' his mouth on a handful of prickly-pear cactus, Bill turned to the cow-boys and asked:

"Who [is] boss around here?"

A big fellow about eight feet tall, with seven pistols and nine bowie-knives in his belt, rose up and, takin' off his hat, said: "Stranger, I was; but you be."

Bill had many adventures with this outfit. It was about this time he staked out New Mexico, and used Arizona for a calf-pasture. It was here that he found his noted horse Widow-Maker. He raised him from a colt on nitroglycerin and dynamite, and Bill was the only man that could throw a leg over him.

There wasn't anythin' that Bill couldn't ride, although I have heard of one occasion when he was thrown. He made a bet that he could ride an Oklahoma cyclone slick-heeled, without a saddle.

He met the cyclone, the worst that was ever known, up on the Kansas line. Bill eared that tornado down and climbed on its back. That cyclone did some pitchin' that is unbelievable, if it were not vouched for by many reliable witnesses.

Down across Texas it went sunfishin', back-flippin', side-windin', knockin' down mountains, blowin' the holes out of the ground, and tyin' rivers into knots. The Staked Plains used to be heavily timbered until that big wind swiped the trees off and left it a bare prairie.

Bill just sat up there, thumbin' that cyclone in the withers, floppin' it across the ears with his hat, and rollin' a cigarette with one hand. He rode it through three States, but over in Arizona it got him.

"A real hard herd of hand-picked hellions." Illustration by Elmer Hader for *The New Century Illustrated Monthly Magazine*, Vol. 106 No. 6 (October 1923).

When it saw it couldn't throw him, it rained out from under him. This is proved by the fact that it washed out the Grand Cañon. Bill came down over in California. The spot where he lit is now known as Death Valley, a hole in the ground more than one hundred feet below sea-level, and the print of his hip-pockets can still be seen in the granite.

I have heard this story disputed in some of its details.

Some historians claim that Bill wasn't thrown; that he slid down on a streak of lightnin' without knockin' the ashes off his cigarette. It is also claimed that the Grand Cañon was dug by Bill one week when he went prospectin'; but the best authorities insist on the first version.

Bill was a great roper. In fact, he invented ropin'. Old-timers who admit they knew him say that his rope was as long as the equator, although the more conservative say that it was at least two feet shorter on one end. He used to rope a herd of cattle at one throw.

This skill once saved the life of a friend. The friend had tried to ride Widow-Maker one day, and was thrown so high he came down on top of Pike's Peak. He was in the middle of a bad fix, because he couldn't get down, and seemed doomed to a lingerin' death on high.

Bill came to the rescue, and usin' only a short calfloop, he roped his friend around the neck and jerked him down to safety in the valley, twenty thousand feet below. This man was always grateful, and became Bill's horse-wrangler at the time he staked out New Mexico.

In his idle moments in New Mexico Bill amused himself puttin' thorns on the trees and horns on the toads. It was on this ranch he dug the Rio Grande and invented the centiped and the tarantula as a joke on his friends.

On another occasion Bill took the job of buildin' the line fence that forms the boundary from El Paso across to the Pacific. He rounded up a herd of prairie-dogs and set them to dig holes, which by nature a prairie-dog likes to do.

Whenever one of them finished a nice hole and settled down to live in it, Bill evicted him and stuck a fence-post in the hole. Everybody admired his foresight except the prairie-dogs, and who cares what a prairie dog thinks?

Many of the border bards who knew Pecos Bill at his best have this account of his death. They say that he met a man from Boston one day, wearing a mail-order cow-boy outfit, and askin' fool questions about the West; and poor old Bill laid down and laughed himself to death.

Week Fifteen:

THE LIFE AND ADVENTURES OF CALAMITY JANE

American Tall Tale

BY CALAMITY JANE

My maiden name was Marthy Cannary, was born in Princeton, Missourri, May 1st, 1852. Father and mother natives of Ohio. Had two brothers and three sisters, I being the oldest of the children. As a child I always had a fondness for adventure and out-door exercise and especial fondness for horses which I began to ride at an early age and continued to do so until I became an expert rider being able to ride the most vicious and stubborn of horses, in fact the greater portion of my life in early times was spent in this manner.

In 1865 we emigrated from our homes in Missourri by the overland route to Virginia City, Montana, taking five months to make the journey. While on the way the greater portion of my time was spent in hunting along with the men and hunters of the party, in fact I was at all times with the men when there was excitement and adventures to be had. By the time we reached Virginia City I was considered a re-markable good shot and a fearless rider for a girl of my age. I remember many occurrences on the journey from Missourri to Montana. Many times in crossing the mountains the conditions of the trail were so bad that we frequently had to lower the wagons over ledges by hand with ropes for they were so rough and rugged that horses were of no use. We also had many exciting times fording streams for many of the streams in our way were noted for quicksands and boggy places, where, unless we were very careful, we would have lost horses and all. Then we had many dangers to encounter in the way of streams swelling on account of heavy rains. On occasions of that kind the men would usually select the best places to cross the streams, myself on more than one occasion have mounted my pony and swam across the stream several times merely to amuse myself and have had many narrow escapes from having both myself and pony washed away to certain death, but as the pioneers of those days had plenty of courage we overcame all obstacles and reached Virginia City in safety.

Mother died at Black Foot, Montana, 1866, where we buried her. I left Montana in Spring of 1866, for Utah, arriving at Salt Lake city during the summer. Remained in Utah until 1867, where my father died, then went to Fort Bridger, Wyoming Territory, where we arrived May 1, 1868. Remained around Fort Bridges during 1868, then went to Piedmont, Wyoming, with U. P. Railway. Joined General Custer as a scout at Fort Russell, Wyoming, in 1870, and started for Arizona for the Indian Campaign. Up to this time I had always worn the costume of my sex. When I joined Custer I donned the uniform of a soldier. It was a bit awkward at first but I soon got to be perfectly at home in men's clothes.

Was in Arizona up to the winter of 1871 and during that time I had a great many adventures with the Indians, for as a scout I had a great many dangerous missions to perform and while I was in many close places always succeeded in getting away safely for by this time I was considered the most reckless and daring rider and one of the best shots in the western country.

After that campaign I returned to Fort Sanders, Wyoming, remained there until spring of 1872, when we were ordered out to the Muscle Shell or Nursey Pursey Indian outbreak. In that war Generals Custer, Miles, Terry and Crook were all engaged. This campaign lasted until fall of 1873.

It was during this campaign that I was christened Calamity Jane. It was on Goose Creek, Wyoming, where the town of Sheridan is now located. Capt. Egan was in command of the Post. We were ordered out to quell an uprising of the Indians, and were out for several days, had numerous skirmishes during which six of the soldiers were killed and several severely wounded. When on returning to the Post we were ambushed about a mile and a half from our destination. When fired upon Capt. Egan was shot. I was riding in advance and on hearing the firing turned in my saddle and saw the Captain reeling in his saddle as though about to fall. I turned my horse and galloped back with all haste to his side and got there in time to catch him as he was falling. I lifted him onto my horse in front of me and succeeded in getting him safely to the Fort. Capt. Egan on recovering, laughingly said: "I name you Calamity Jane, the heroine of the plains." I have borne that name up to the present time. We were afterwards ordered to Fort Custer, where Custer city now stands, where we arrived in the spring of 1874; remained around Fort Custer all summer and were ordered to Fort Russell in fall of 1874, where we remained until spring of 1875; was then ordered to the Black Hills to protect miners, as that country was controlled by the Sioux Indians and the government had to send the soldiers to protect the lives of the miners and settlers in that section. Remained there until fall of 1875 and wintered at Fort Laramie. In spring of 1876, we were ordered north with General Crook to join Gen'ls Miles, Terry and Custer at Big Horn river. During this march I swam the Platte river at Fort Fetterman as I was the bearer of important dispatches. I had a ninety mile ride to make, being wet and cold, I contracted a severe illness and was sent back in Gen. Crook's ambulance to Fort Fetterman where I laid in the hospital for fourteen days. When able to ride I started for Fort Laramie where I met Wm. Hickock, better known as Wild Bill, and we started for Deadwood, where we arrived about June.

During the month of June I acted as a pony express rider carrying the U. S. mail between Deadwood and Custer, a distance of fifty miles, over one of the roughest trails in the Black Hills country. As many of the riders before me had been held up and robbed of their packages, mail and money that they carried, for that was the only means of getting mail and money between these points. It was considered the most dangerous route in the Hills, but as my reputation as a rider and quick shot was well known, I was molested very little, for the toll gatherers looked on me as being a good fellow, and they knew that I never missed my mark. I made the round trip every two days which was considered pretty good riding in that country. Remained around Deadwood all that summer visiting all the camps within an area of one hundred miles. My friend, Wild Bill, remained in Deadwood during the summer with the exception of occasional visits to the camps. On the 2nd of August, while setting at a gambling table in the Bell Union saloon, in Deadwood, he was shot in the back of the head by the notorious Jack McCall, a desperado. I was in Deadwood at the time and on hearing of the killing made my way at once to the scene of the shooting and found that my friend had been killed by McCall. I at once started to look for the assassin and found him at Shurdy's butcher shop and grabbed a meat cleaver and made him throw up his hands; through the excitement on hearing of Bill's death, having left my weapons on the post of my bed. He was then taken to a log cabin and locked up, well secured as every one thought, but he got away and was afterwards caught at Fagan's ranch on Horse Creek, on the old Cheyenne road and was then taken to Yankton, Dak., where he was tried, sentenced and hung.

I remained around Deadwood locating claims, going from camp to camp until the spring of 1877, where one morning, I saddled my horse and rode towards Crook city. I had gone about twelve miles from Deadwood, at the mouth of Whitewood creek, when I met the overland mail running from Cheyenne to Deadwood. The horses on a run, about two hundred yards from the station; upon looking closely I saw they were pursued by Indians. The horses ran to the barn as was their custom. As the horses stopped I rode along side of the coach and found the driver John Slaughter, lying face downwards in the boot of the stage, he having been shot by the Indians. When the stage got to the station the Indians hid in the bushes. I immediately removed all baggage from the coach except the mail. I then took the driver's seat and with all haste drove to Deadwood, carrying the six passengers and the dead driver.

I left Deadwood In the fall of 1877, and went to Bear Butte Creek with the 7th Cavalry. During the fall and winter we built Fort Meade and the town of Sturgis. In 1878 I left the command and went to Rapid city and put in the year prospecting.

In 1879 I went to Fort Pierre and drove trains from Rapid City to Fort Pierre for Frank Wite then drove teams from Fort Pierce to Sturgis for Fred Evans. This teaming was done with oxen as they were better fitted for the work than horses, owing to the rough nature of the country.

In 1881 I went to Wyoming and returned in 1882 to Miles city and took up a ranch on the Yellow Stone, raising stock and cattle, also kept a way side inn, where the weary traveler could be accommodated with food, drink, or trouble if he looked for it. Left the ranch in 1883, went to California, going through the States and territories, reached Ogden the latter part of 1883, and San Francisco in 1884. Left San Francisco in the summer of 1884 for Texas, stopping at Fort Yuma, Arizona, the hottest spot in the United States. Stopping at all points of interest until I reached El Paso in the fall. While in El Paso, I met Mr. Clinton Burk, a native of Texas, who I married in August 1885. As I thought I had travelled through life long enough alone and thought it was about time to take a partner for the rest of my days. We remained in Texas leading a quiet home life until 1889. On October 28th, 1887, I became the mother of a girl baby, the very image of its father, at least that is what he said, but who has the temper of its mother.

When we left Texas we went to Boulder, Colo., where we kept a hotel until 1893, after which we travelled through Wyoming, Montana, Idaho, Washington, Oregon, then back to Montano, then to Dakato, arriving in Deadwood October 9th, 1895, after an absence of seventeen years.

My arrival in Deadwood after an absence so many years created quite an excitement among my many friends of the past, to such an extent that a vast number of the citizens who had come to Deadwood during my absence who had heard so much of Calamity Jane and her many adventures in former years were anxious to see me. Among the many whom I met were several gentlemen from eastern cities, who advised me to allow myself to be placed before the public in such a manner as to give the people of the eastern cities an opportunity of seeing the Woman Scout who was made so famous through her daring career in the West and Black Hill countries.

An agent of Kohl & Middleton, the celebrated Museum men came to Deadwood, through the solicitation of the gentleman whom I had met there and arrangements were made to place me before the public in this manner. My first engagement began at the Palace Museum, Minneapolis, January 20th, 1896, under Kohl and Middleton's management.

Week Fifteen:
JOHN HENRY

When John Henry was a little babe,
　　A-holding to his mama's hand,
Says, "If I live till I'm twenty-one,
　　　I'm going to make a steel-driving man, my babe,
　　　I'm going to make a steel-driving man."

When John Henry was a little boy,
　　A-sitting on his father's knee,
Says, "The Big Bend Tunnel on the C. & O. Road
　　　Is going to be the death of me, my babe," etc.

John he made a steel-driving man,
　　They took him to the tunnel to drive;
He drove so hard he broke his heart,
　　　He laid down his hammer and he died, my babe, etc.

O now John Henry is a steel-driving man,
　　He belongs to the steel-driving crew,
And every time his hammer comes down,
　　　You can see that steel walking through, etc.

The steam drill standing on the right-hand side,
　　John Henry standing on the left;
He says, "I'll beat that steam drill down,
　　　Or I'll die with my hammer in my breast," etc.

He placed his drill on the top of the rock,
    The steam drill standing close at hand;
He beat it down one inch and a half
    And laid down his hammer like a man, etc.

Johnny looked up to his boss-man and said,
    "O boss-man, how can it be?
For the rock is so hard and the steel is so tough,
    I can feel my muscles giving way."

Johnny looked down to his turner and said,
    "O turner, how can it be?
The rock is so hard and the steel is so tough
    That everybody's turning after me."

They took poor Johnny to the steep hillside,
    He looked to his heavens above;
He says, "Take my hammer and wrap it in gold
    And give it to the girl I love."

They took his hammer and wrapped it in gold
    And gave it to Julia Ann;
And the last word Johnny said to her
    Was, "Julia, do the best you can."

"If I die a railroad man,
    Go bury me under the tie,
So I can hear old Number Four,
    As she goes rolling by.

"If I die a railroad man,
    Go bury me under the sand,
With a pick and shovel at my head and feet,
    And a nine-pound hammer in my hand."

RETOLD BY JOSIAH H. COMBS (1886–1960)

Week Sixteen:

Paul Bunyan's Family and Inventions

American Tall Tale

BY W. B. LAUGHEAD

The family life of Paul Bunyan, from all accounts, has been very happy. A charming glimpse of Mrs. Bunyan is given by Mr. E. S. Shepard of Rhinelander, Wis., who tells of working in Paul's camp on Round River in '62, the Winter of the Black Snow. Paul put him wheeling prune pits away from the cook camp. After he had worked at this job for three months Paul had him haul them back again as Mrs. Bunyan, who was cooking at the camp, wanted to use them to make the hot fires necessary to cook her famous soft nosed pancakes.

Mrs. Bunyan, at this time used to call the men to dinner by blowing into a woodpecker hole in an old hollow stub that stood near the door. In this stub there was a nest of owls that had one short wing and flew in circles. When Mr. Shepard made a sketch of Paul, Mrs. Bunyan, with wifely solicitude for his appearance, parted Paul's hair with a handaxe and combed it with an old cross-cut saw.

From other sources we have fragmentary glimpses of Jean, Paul's youngest son. When Jean was three weeks old, he jumped from his cradle one night and seizing an axe, chopped the four posts out from under his father's bed. The incident greatly tickled Paul, who used to brag about it to anyone who would listen to him. "The boy is going to be a great logger someday," he would declare with fatherly pride.

The last we heard of Jean he was working for a lumber outfit in the South, lifting logging trains past one another on a single-track railroad.

WHEN PAUL INVENTED LOGGING HE HAD TO INVENT ALL THE TOOLS and figure out all his own methods. There were no precedents. At the start his outfit consisted of Babe and his big axe.

No two logging jobs can be handled exactly the same way so Paul adapted his operations to local conditions. In the mountains he used Babe to pull the kinks out of the crooked logging roads; on the Big Onion he began the system of hauling a section of land at a time to the landings and in North Dakota he used the Seven Axemen.

The Grindstone was invented by Paul the winter he logged off North Dakota. Before that Paul's axemen had to sharpen their axes by rolling rocks downhill and running alongside of them. When they got to "Big Dick," as the lumberjacks called Dakota, hills and rocks were so hard to find that Paul rigged up the revolving rock.

This was much appreciated by the Seven Axemen as it enabled them to grind an axe in a week, but the grindstone was not much of a hit with the Little Chore Boy whose job it was to turn it. The first stone was so big that working at full speed, every time it turned around once it was payday.

The Little Chore Boy led a strenuous life. He was only a kid and like all youngsters putting in their first winter in the woods, he was put over the jumps by the old-timers. His regular work was heavy enough,

Illustrations by W. B. Laughead in *The Marvelous Exploits of Paul Bunyan* (Minneapolis: Red River Lumber Company, 1922).

splitting all the wood for the camp, carrying water and packing lunch to the men, but his hazers sent him on all kinds of wild goose errands to all parts of the works, looking for a "left-handed peavy" or a "bundle of cross-hauls."

He had to take a lot of good-natured roughneck wit about his size for he only weighed 800 pounds and a couple of surcingles made a belt for him. What he lacked in size he made up in grit and the men secretly respected his gameness. They said he might make a pretty good man if he ever got any growth and considered it a necessary education to give him a lot of extra chores.

Often in the evening, after his day's work and long hours put in turning the grindstone and keeping up fires in the camp stoves—that required four cords of wood apiece to kindle a fire, he could be found with one of Big Ole's small 600-pound anvils in his lap pegging up shoes with railroad spikes.

It was a long time before they solved the problem of turning logging sleds around in the road. When a sled returned from the landing and put on a load they had to wait until Paul came along to pick up the four horses and the load and head them the other way. Judson M. Goss says he worked for Paul the winter he invented the round turn.

All of Paul's inventions were successful except when he decided to run three ten-hour shifts a day and installed the Aurora Borealis. After a number of trials, the plan was abandoned because the lights were not dependable.

"The Seven Axemen of the Red River" they were called because they had a camp on Red River with the three-hundred cooks and the Little Chore Boy. The whole State was cut over from the one camp and the husky seven chopped from dark to dark and walked to and from work.

Their axes were so big it took a week to grind one of them. Each man had three axes and two helpers to carry the spare axes to the river when they got red hot from chopping. Even in those days they had to watch out for forest fires. The axes were hung on long rope handles. Each axeman would march through the timber whirling his axe around him till the hum of it sounded like one of Paul's for-and-aft mosquitoes, and at every step a quarter-section of timber was cut.

The height, weight and chest measurement of the Seven Axemen are not known. Authorities differ. History agrees that they kept a cord of four-foot wood on the table for toothpicks. After supper they would sit on the deacon seat in the bunk shanty and sing "Shanty Boy" and

"Bung Yer Eye" till the folks in the settlements down on the Atlantic would think another nor'wester was blowing up.

As a hunter, Paul would make old Nimrod himself look like a city dude lost from his guide. He was also a good fisherman. Old-timers tell of seeing Paul as a small boy, fishing off the Atlantic Coast. He would sail out early in the morning in his three-mast schooner and wade back before breakfast with his boat full of fish on his shoulder.

About this time, he got his shotgun that required four dishpans full of powder and a keg of spikes to load each barrel. With this gun he could shoot geese so high in the air they would spoil before reaching the ground.

Tracking was Paul's favorite sport and no trail was too old or too dim for him to follow. He once came across the skeleton of a moose that had died of old age and, just for curiosity, picked up the tracks of the animal and spent the whole afternoon following its trail back to the place where it was born.

IT IS NO PICNIC TO TACKLE THE WILDERNESS and turn the very forest itself into a commercial commodity delivered at the market. A logger needs plenty of brains and back bone.

Paul Bunyan had his setbacks the same as every logger only his were worse. Being a pioneer, he had to invent all his stuff as he went along. Many a time his plans were upset by the mistakes of some swivel-headed strawboss or incompetent foreman. The winter of the blue snow, Shot Gunderson had charge in the Big Tadpole River country. He landed all of his logs in a lake and in the spring when ready to drive he boomed the logs three times around the lake before he discovered there was no outlet to it. High hills surrounded the lake and the drivable stream was ten miles away. Apparently, the logs were a total loss.

Then Paul came on the job himself and got busy. Calling in Sourdough Sam, the cook who made everything but coffee out of sourdough, he ordered him to mix enough sourdough to fill the big water tank. Hitching Babe to the tank he hauled it over and dumped it into the lake. When it "riz," as Sam said, a mighty lava-like stream poured forth and carried the logs over the hills to the river. There is a landlocked lake in Northern Minnesota that is called "Sourdough Lake" to this day.

Chris Crosshaul was a careless cuss. He took a big drive down the Mississippi for Paul and when the logs were delivered in the New Orleans boom it was found that he had driven the wrong logs. The owners looked at the bark marks and refused to accept them. It was up to Paul to drive them back upstream.

No one but Paul Bunyan would ever tackle a job like that. To drive logs upstream is impossible, but if you think a little thing like an impossibility could stop him, you don't know Paul Bunyan. He simply fed Babe a good big salt ration and drove him to the upper Mississippi to drink. Babe drank the river dry and sucked all the water upstream. The logs came upriver faster than they went down.

PAUL BUNYAN STARTED TRAVELING BEFORE THE STEAM CARS WERE INVENTED. He developed his own means of transportation and the railroads have never been able to catch up. Time is so valuable to Paul he has no time to fool around at sixty miles an hour.

In the early days he rode on the back of Babe, the Big Blue Ox. This had its difficulties because he had to use a telescope to keep Babe's hind legs in view and the hooves of the ox created such havoc that after the settlements came into different parts of the country there were heavy damage claims to settle every trip.

Snowshoes were useful in winter but one trip on the webs cured Paul of depending upon them for transcontinental hikes. He started from Minnesota for Westwood one Spring morning. There was still snow in the woods, so Paul wore his snowshoes. He soon ran out of the snow belt but kept right on without reducing speed. Crossing the desert, the heat became oppressive, his mackinaws grew heavy and the snowshoes dragged his feet but it was too late to turn back.

When he arrived in California, he discovered that the sun and hot sand had warped one of his shoes and pulled one foot out of line at every step, so instead of traveling on a bee line and hitting Westwood exactly, he came out at San Francisco. This made it necessary for him to travel an extra three hundred miles north. It was late that night when he pulled into Westwood and he had used up a whole day coming from Minnesota.

Paul's fast foot work made him a "good man on the round stuff" and in spite of his weight he had no trouble running around on the floating logs, even the small ones. It was said that Paul could spin a log till the bark came off and then run ashore on the bubbles. He once threw a peavy handle into the Mississippi at St. Louis and standing on it, poled up to Brainerd, Minnesota. Paul was a "white water bucko" and rode water so rough it would tear an ordinary man in two to drink out of the river.

IF PAUL BUNYAN DID NOT INVENT GEOGRAPHY HE CREATED A LOT OF IT. The Great Lakes were first constructed to provide a water hole for Babe the Big Blue Ox. Just what year his work was done is not known but they were in use prior to the Year of the Two Winters.

The Winter Paul Bunyan logged off North Dakota he hauled water for his ice roads from the Great Lakes. One day when Brimstone Bill had Babe hitched to one of the old water tanks and was making his early morning trip, the tank sprung a leak when they were halfway across Minnesota. Bill saved himself from drowning by climbing Babe's tail but all efforts to patch up the tank were in vain, so the old tank was abandoned and replaced by one of the new ones. This was the beginning of the Mississippi River and the truth of this is established by the fact that the old Mississippi is still flowing.

The cooks in Paul's camps used a lot of water and to make things handy, they used to dig wells near the cook shanty. At headquarters on the Big Auger, on top of the hill near the mouth of the Little Gimlet, Paul dug a well so deep that it took all day for the bucket to fall to the water, and a week to haul it up. They had to run so many buckets that the well was forty feet in diameter. It was shored up with tamarac poles and when the camp was abandoned Paul pulled up this cribbing. Travelers who have visited the spot say that the sand has blown away until 178 feet of the well is sticking up into the air, forming a striking landmark.

THE WINTER OF THE DEEP SNOW EVERY-THING WAS BURIED. Paul had to dig down to find the tops of the tallest White Pines. He had the snow dug away around them and lowered his sawyers down to the base of the trees. When the tree was cut off, he hauled it to the surface with a long parbuckle chain to which Babe, mounted on snowshoes, was hitched. It was impossible to get enough stove pipe to reach to the top of the snow, so Paul had Big Ole make stovepipe by boring out logs with a long six-inch auger.

The year of the Two Winters they had winter all summer and then in the fall it turned colder. One day Big Joe set the boiling coffeepot on the stove and it froze so quick that the ice was hot. That was right after Paul had built the Great Lakes and that winter, they froze clear to the bottom. They never would have thawed out if Paul had not chopped out the ice and hauled it out on shore for the sun to melt. He finally got all the ice thawed but he had to put in all new fish.

The next spring was the year the rain came up from China. It rained so hard and so long that the grass was all washed out by the roots and Paul had a great time feeding his cattle. Babe had to learn to eat pancakes like Benny. That was the time Paul used the straw hats for an emergency ration.

When Paul's drive came down, folks in the settlements were astonished to see all the river-pigs wearing huge straw hats. The reason for this was soon apparent. When the fodder ran out every man was politely requested to toss his hat into the ring. Hundreds of straw hats were used to make a lunch for Babe.

When paul bunyan took up efficiency engineering, he went at the job with all his customary thoroughness. He did not fool around clocking the crew with a stopwatch, counting motions and deducting the ones used for borrowing chews, going for drinks, dodging the boss and preparing for quitting time. He decided to cut out labor altogether.

"What's the use," said Paul, "of all this sawing, swamping, skidding, decking, grading and icing roads, loading, hauling and landing? The object of the game is to get the trees to the landing, ain't it? Well, why not do it and get it off your mind?"

So, he hitched Babe to a section of land and snaked in the whole 640 acres at one drag. At the landing the trees were cut off just like shearing a sheep and the denuded section hauled back to its original place. This simplified matters and made the work a lot easier. Six trips a day, six days a week just cleaned up a township for section 37 was never

PAUL BUNYAN SAYS:
" IM GOING TO CHANGE "BABE'S"
NAME TO "FAITH" SINCE
HE MOVED THE MOUNTAIN."

hauled back to the woods on Saturday night but was left on the landing to wash away in the early spring when the drive went out.

FROM 1917 TO 1920 PAUL BUNYAN WAS BUSY toting the supplies and building camps for a bunch of husky young fellow-Americans who had a contract on the other side of the Atlantic, showing a certain prominent European (who is now logging in Holland) how they log in the United States.

After his service overseas with the A. E. F., Paul couldn't get back to the States quick enough. Airplanes were too slow, so Paul embarked in his Bark Canoe, the one he used on the Big Onion the year he drove logs upstream. When he threw the old paddle into high, he sure rambled, and the sea was covered with dead fish that broke their backs trying to watch him coming and going.

As he shoved off from France, Paul sent a wireless to New York but passed the Statue of Liberty three lengths ahead of the message. From New York to Westwood he traveled on skis. When the home folks asked him if the Allegheny Mountains and the Rockies had bothered him, Paul replied, "I didn't notice any mountains, but the trail was a little bumpy in a couple of spots."

Illustrations by W. B. Laughead in *The Marvelous Exploits of Paul Bunyan* (Minneapolis: Red River Lumber Company, 1922).

Week Sixteen:
PAUL BUNYAN'S ANIMALS AND INSECTS
American Tall Tale
BY W. B. LAUGHEAD

Babe, the big blue ox constituted Paul Bunyan's assets and liabilities. History disagrees as to when, where and how Paul first acquired this bovine locomotive, but his subsequent record is reliably established. Babe could pull anything that had two ends to it.

Babe was seven axehandles wide between the eyes according to some authorities; others equally dependable say forty-two axehandles and a plug of tobacco. Like other historical contradictions this comes from using different standards. Seven of Paul's axehandles were equal to a little more than forty-two of the ordinary kind.

When cost sheets were figured on Babe, Johnny Inkslinger found that upkeep and overhead were expensive but the charges for operation and depreciation were low and the efficiency was very high. How else could Paul have hauled logs to the landing a whole section (640 acres) at a time? He also used Babe to pull the kinks out of

the crooked logging roads and it was on a job of this kind that Babe pulled a chain of three-inch links out into a straight bar.

They could never keep Babe more than one night at a camp for he would eat in one day all the feed one crew could tote to camp in a year. For a snack between meals he would eat fifty bales of hay, wire and all and six men with picaroons were kept busy picking the wire out of his teeth. Babe was a great pet and very docile as a general thing, but he seemed to have a sense of humor and frequently got into mischief, He would sneak up behind a drive and drink all the water out of the river, leaving the logs high and dry. It was impossible to build an ox-sling big enough to hoist Babe off the ground for shoeing, but after they logged off Dakota there was room for Babe to lie down for this operation.

Once in a while Babe would run away and be gone all day roaming all over the Northwestern country. His tracks were so far apart that it was impossible to follow him and so deep that a man falling into one could only be hauled out with difficulty and a long rope. Once a settler and his wife and baby fell into one of these tracks and the son got out when he was fifty-seven years old and reported the accident. These tracks, today form the thousands of lakes in the "Land of the Sky-Blue Water."

BECAUSE HE WAS SO MUCH YOUNGER THAN BABE and was brought to camp when a small calf, Benny was always called the Little Blue Ox although he was quite a chunk of an animal. Benny could not, or rather, would not haul as much as Babe nor was he as tractable but he could eat more.

Paul got Benny for nothing from a farmer near Bangor, Maine. There was not enough milk for the little fellow, so he had to be weaned when three days old. The farmer only had forty acres of hay and by the time Benny was a week old he had to dispose of him for lack of food. The calf was undernourished and only weighed two tons when Paul got him. Paul drove from Bangor out to his headquarters camp near Devil's Lake, North Dakota that night and led Benny behind the sleigh. Western air agreed with the little calf and every time Paul looked back at him, he was two feet taller.

When they arrived at camp Benny was given a good feed of buffalo milk and flapjacks and put into a barn by himself. Next morning the barn was gone. Later it was discovered on Benny's back as he scampered over the clearings. He had outgrown his barn in one night.

Benny was very notional and would never pull a load unless there was snow on the ground so after the spring thaws, they had to white wash the logging roads to fool him.

Gluttony killed Benny. He had a mania for pancakes and one cook crew of two hundred men was kept busy making cakes for him. One night he pawed and bellowed and threshed his tail about till the wind of it blew down what pine Paul had left standing in Dakota. At break-fast time he broke loose, tore down the cook shanty and began bolting pancakes. In his greed he swallowed the red-hot stove. Indigestion set in and nothing could save him. What disposition was made of his body is a matter of dispute. One old-timer claims that the outfit he works for bought a hind quarter of the carcass in 1857 and made corned beef of it. He thinks they have several carloads of it, left.

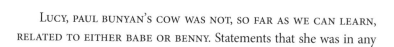

Another authority states that the body of Benny was dragged to a safe distance from the North Dakota camp and buried. When the earth was shoveled back it made a mound that formed the Black Hills in South Dakota.

LUCY, PAUL BUNYAN'S COW WAS NOT, SO FAR AS WE CAN LEARN, RELATED TO EITHER BABE OR BENNY. Statements that she was in any way their mother are without basis in fact. The two oxen had been in Paul's possession for a long time before Lucy arrived on the scene.

No reliable data can be found as to the pedigree of this remarkable dairy animal. There are no official records of her butterfat production nor is it known where or how Paul got her.

Paul always said that Lucy was part Jersey and part wolf. Maybe so. Her actions and methods of living seemed to justify the allegation of wolf ancestry, for she had an insatiable appetite and a roving disposition. Lucy ate everything in sight and could never be fed at the same camp with Babe or Benny. In fact, they quit trying to feed her at all but let her forage her own living. The Winter of the Deep Snow, when even the tallest White Pines were buried, Brimstone Bill outfitted Lucy with a set of Babe's old snowshoes and a pair of green goggles and turned her out to graze on the snowdrifts. At first, she had some trouble with the new foot gear but once she learned to run them and shift gears without wrecking herself, she answered the call of the limitless snow  fields and ran away all over North America until Paul decorated her with a bell borrowed from a buried church.

In spite of short rations, she gave enough milk to keep six men busy skimming the cream. If she had been kept in a barn and fed regularly, she might have made a milking record. When she fed on the evergreen trees and her milk got so strong of White Pine and Balsam that the men used it for cough medicine and liniment, they quit serving the milk on the table and made butter out of it. By using this butter, to grease the logging roads when the snow and ice thawed off, Paul was able to run big logging sleds all summer.

WHAT IS CAMP WITHOUT A DOG? Paul Bunyan loved dogs as well as the next man but never would have one around that could not earn its keep. Paul's dogs had to work, hunt or catch rats. It took a good dog to kill the rats and mice in Paul's camp for the rodents picked up scraps of the buffalo milk pancakes and grew to be as big as two-year-old bears.

Elmer, the moose terrier, practiced up on the rats when he was a small pup and was soon able to catch a moose on the run and finish it with one shake. Elmer loafed around the cook camp and if the meat supply happened to run low the cook would put the dog out the door and say, "Bring in a moose." Elmer would run into the timber, catch a moose and bring it in and repeat the performance until, after a few minutes work, the cook figured he had enough for a mess and would call the dog in.

Sport, the reversible dog was really the best hunter. He was part wolf and part elephant hound and was raised on bear milk. One night when Sport was quite young, he was playing around in the horse barn and Paul, mistaking him for a mouse, threw a band axe at him. The axe cut the dog in two but Paul, instantly realizing what had happened, quickly stuck the two halves together, gave the pup first aid and bandaged him up. With careful nursing the dog soon recovered and then it was seen that Paul in his haste had twisted the two halves so that the hind legs pointed straight up. This proved to be an advantage for the dog learned to run on one pair of legs for a while and then flop over without loss of speed and run on the other pair. Because of this he never tired and anything he started after got caught.

PAUL BUNYAN'S TRAINED ANTS ARE PROVING SO SUCCESSFUL that they may replace donkeys and tractors on the rugged slopes of the Sierras. Inspired by his success with Bees and Mosquitoes, Paul has developed a breed of Ants that stand six feet tall and weigh 200 pounds.

To overcome their habit of hibernating all Winter, Paul supplied the Ants with Mackinaws made with three pairs of sleeves or legs. They eat nothing but Copenhagen Snuff. The Ants (or Uncles as they prefer to be called) can run to the Westwood shops with a damaged locomotive quicker than the Wrecking Crew can come out. They do not patronize bootleggers or require time off to fix their automobiles.

HAVE YOU EVER ENCOUNTERED THE MOSQUITO OF THE NORTH COUNTRY? You thought they were pretty well-developed animals with keen appetites, didn't you? Then you can appreciate what Paul Bunyan was up against when he was surrounded by the vast swarms of the giant ancestors of the present race of mosquitoes, getting their first taste of human victims. The present mosquito is but a degenerate remnant of the species. Now they rarely weigh more than a pound or measure more than fourteen or fifteen inches from tip to tip.

Paul had to keep his men and oxen in the camps with doors and windows barred. Men armed with pikepoles and axes fought off the insects that tore the shakes off the roof in their efforts to gain entrance. The big buck mosquitoes fought among themselves and trampled down the weaker members of the swarm and to this alone Paul Bunyan and his crew owe their lives.

Paul determined to conquer the mosquitoes before another season arrived. He thought of the big Bumble Bees back home and sent for several yoke of them. These, he hoped would destroy the mosquitoes. Sourdough Sam brought out two pair of bees, overland on foot. There was no other way to travel for the flight of the beasts could not be controlled. Their wings were strapped with surcingles, they checked their stingers with Sam and walking shoes were provided for them. Sam brought them through without losing a bee.

The cure was worse than the original trouble. The Mosquitoes and the Bees made a hit with each other. They soon intermarried and their offspring, as often happens, were worse than their parents. They had stingers fore-and-aft and could get you coming or going.

Their bee blood caused their downfall in the long run. Their craving for sweets could only be satisfied by sugar and molasses in large quantities, for what is a flower to an insect with a ten-gallon stomach? One day the whole tribe flew across Lake Superior to attack a fleet of ships bringing sugar to Paul's camps. They destroyed the ships but ate so much sugar they could not fly, and all were drowned.

One pair of the original bees were kept at headquarters camp and provided honey for the pancakes for many years.

"Barbara Frietchie." Illustration by N. C. Wyeth in *Poems of American Patriotism*, edited by
Brander Matthews (New York: C. Scribner's Sons, 1923).

Week Sixteen

BARBARA FRIETCHIE

Up from the meadows rich
with corn,
Clear in the cool September
morn.

The clustered spires of Frederick
stand
Green-walled by the hills of
Maryland.

Round about them orchards
sweep,
Apple- and peach-tree fruited
deep.

Fair as a garden of the Lord
To the eyes of the famished rebel
horde,

On that pleasant morn of the
early fall
When Lee marched over the
mountain-wall,—

Over the mountains winding
down,
Horse and foot, into Frederick
town.

Forty flags with their silver stars,
Forty flags with their crimson
bars,

Flapped in the morning wind:
the sun
Of noon looked down, and saw
not one.

Up rose old Barbara Frietchie
then,
Bowed with her fourscore years
and ten;

Bravest of all in Frederick town.
She took up the flag the men
hauled down;

In her attic window the staff she
     set,
To show that one heart was loyal
     yet.

Up the street came the rebel
     tread,
Stonewall Jackson riding ahead.

Under his slouched hat left and
     right
He glanced: the old flag met his
     sight.

"Halt!" — the dust-brown ranks
     stood fast.
"Fire!" — out blazed the
     rifle-blast.

It shivered the window, pane
     and sash;
It rent the banner with seam and
     gash.

Quick, as it fell, from the broken
     staff
Dame Barbara snatched the
     silken scarf;

She leaned far out on the
     window-sill,
And shook it forth with a royal
     will.

"Shoot, if you must, this old gray
     head,
But spare your country's flag,"
     she said.

A shade of sadness, a blush of
     shame,
Over the face of the leader came;

The nobler nature within him
     stirred
To life at that woman's deed and
     word:

"Who touches a hair of yon gray
     head
Dies like a dog! March on!" he
     said.

All day long through Frederick
     street
Sounded the tread of marching
     feet:

All day long that free flag tost
Over the heads of the rebel host.

Ever its torn folds rose and fell
On the loyal winds that loved it
     well;

And through the hill-gaps
    sunset light
Shone over it with a warm
    good-night.

Barbara Frietchie's work is o'er.
And the Rebel rides on his raids
    no more.

Honor to her! and let a tear
Fall, for her sake, on Stonewall's
    bier.

Over Barbara Frietchie's grave.
Flag of Freedom and Union,
    wave!

Peace and order and beauty
    draw
Round thy symbol of light and
    law;

And ever the stars above look
    down
On thy stars below in Frederick
    town!

JOHN GREENLEAF WHITTIER
(1807–1892)

Illustrations by W. B. Laughead in *The Marvelous Exploits of Paul Bunyan* (Minneapolis: Red River Lumber Company, 1922).

Week Seventeen

FEEDING PAUL BUNYAN'S CREW

American Tall Tale

BY W. B. LAUGHEAD

Feeding Paul Bunyan's crews was a complicated job. At no two camps were conditions the same. The winter he logged off North Dakota he had 300 cooks making pancakes for the Seven Axemen and the little Chore-boy. At headquarters on the Big Onion he had one cook and 462 cookees feeding a crew so big that Paul himself never knew within several hundred either way, how many men he had.

At Big Onion camp there was a lot of mechanical equipment and the trouble was a man who could handle the machinery cooked just like a machinist too. One cook got lost between the flour bin and the root cellar and nearly starved to death before he was found.

Cooks came and went. Some were good and others just able to get by. Paul never kept a poor one, very long. There was one jigger who seemed to have learned to do nothing but boil. He made soup out of everything and did most of his work with a dipper. When the big tote-sled broke through the ice on Bull Frog Lake with a load of split peas, he served warmed up, lake water till the crew struck. His idea of a lunch box was a jug or a rope to freeze soup onto like a candle. Some cooks used too much grease. It was said of one of these that he had to wear calked shoes to keep from sliding out of the cook-shanty and rub sand on his hands when he picked anything up.

There are two kinds of camp cooks, the Baking Powder Bums and the Sourdough Stiffs. Sourdough Sam belonged to the latter school. He made everything but coffee out of Sourdough. He had only one arm and one leg, the other members having been lost when his sourdough barrel blew up. Sam officiated at Tadpole River headquarters, the winter Shot Gunderson took charge.

After all others had failed at Big Onion camp, Paul hired his cousin Big Joe who came from three weeks below Quebec. This boy sure put a mean scald on the chuck. He was the only man who could make pancakes fast enough to feed the crew. He had Big Ole, the blacksmith, make him a griddle that was so big you couldn't see across it when the steam was thick. The batter, stirred in drums like concrete mixers, was poured on with cranes and spouts.

At this camp the flunkeys wore roller skates and an idea of the size of the tables is gained from the fact that they distributed the pepper with four-horse teams.

Sending out lunch and timing the meals was rendered difficult by the size of the works which required three crews—one going to work, one on the job and one coming back. Joe had to start the bull-cook out with the lunch sled two weeks ahead of dinner time. To call the men who came in at noon was another problem. Big Ole made a dinner horn so big that no one could blow it but Big Joe or Paul himself. The first time Joe blew it he blew down ten acres of pine. The Red River people wouldn't stand for that so the next time he blew straight up but this caused severe cyclones and storms at sea so Paul had to junk the horn and ship it East where later it was made into a tin roof for a big Union Depot.

When Big Joe came to Westwood with Paul, he started something. About that time, you may have read in the papers about a volcanic eruption at Mt. Lassen, heretofore extinct for many years. That was where Big Joe dug his bean-hole and when the steam worked out of the bean kettle and up through the ground, everyone thought the old hill had turned volcano. Every time Joe drops a biscuit they talk of earthquakes.

It was always thought that the quality of the food at Paul's Camps had a lot to do with the strength and endurance of the men. No doubt it did, but they were a husky lot to start with. As the feller said about fish for a brain food, "It won't do you no good unless there is a germ there to start with."

There must have been something to the food theory for the chipmunks that ate the prune pits got so big they killed all the wolves and years later the settlers shot them for tigers.

A visitor at one of Paul's camps was astonished to see a crew of men unloading four-horse logging sleds at the cook-shanty. They appeared to be rolling logs into a trap door from which poured clouds of steam.

"That's a heck of a place to land logs," he remarked.

"Them ain't logs," grinned a bull-cook, "them's sausages for the teamsters' breakfast."

At Paul's camp up where the little Gimlet empties into the Big Auger, newcomers used to kick because they were never served beans. The bosses and the men could never be interested in beans. E. E. Terrill tells us the reason:

Once when the cook quit, they had to detail a substitute to the job temporarily. There was one man who was no good anywhere. He had failed at every job. Chris Crosshaul, the foreman, acting on the theory that every man is good somewhere, figured that this guy must be a cook, for it was the only job he had not tried. So, he was put to work and the first thing he tackled was beans. He filled up a big kettle with beans and added some water. When the heat took hold the beans swelled up till, they lifted off the roof and bulged out the walls. There was no way to get into the place to cook anything else, so the whole crew turned in to eat up the half-cooked beans. By keeping at it steady they cleaned them up in a week and rescued the would-be-cook. After that no one seemed to care much for beans.

It used to be a big job to haul prune pits and coffee grounds away from Paul's camps. It required a big crew of men and either Babe or Benny to do the hauling. Finally, Paul decided it was cheaper to build new camps and move every month.

The winter Paul logged off North Dakota with the Seven Axemen, the Little Chore Boy and the 300 cooks, he worked the cooks in three shifts—one for each meal. The Seven Axemen were hearty eaters; a portion of bacon was one side of a 1600-pound pig. Paul shipped a stern-wheel steamboat up Red River and they put it in the soup kettle to stir the soup.

Like other artists, cooks are temperamental and some of them are full of cussedness but the only ones who could sass Paul Bunyan and get away with it were the stars like Big Joe and Sourdough Sam.

The lunch sled,—most popular institution in the lumber industry! Its arrival at the noon rendezvous has been hailed with joy by hungry men on every logging job since Paul invented it. What if the warm food freezes on your tin plate, the keen cold air has sharpened your appetite to enjoy it. The crew that toted lunch for Paul Bunyan had so far to travel and so many to feed they hauled a complete kitchen on the lunch sled, cooks and all.

Week Seventeen

THE GLORIOUS WHITEWASHER

American Folk Tale

BY MARK TWAIN

Saturday morning was come, and all the summer world was bright and fresh, and brimming with life. There was a song in every heart; and if the heart was young the music issued at the lips. There was cheer in every face and a spring in every step. The locust-trees were in bloom and the fragrance of the blossoms filled the air. Cardiff Hill, beyond the village and above it, was green with vegetation and it lay just far enough away to seem a Delectable Land, dreamy, reposeful, and inviting.

Tom appeared on the sidewalk with a bucket of whitewash and a long-handled brush. He surveyed the fence, and all gladness left him and a deep melancholy settled down upon his spirit. Thirty yards of board fence nine feet high. Life to him seemed hollow, and existence but a burden. Sighing, he dipped his brush and passed it along the topmost plank; repeated the operation; did it again; compared the insignificant whitewashed streak with the far-reaching continent of unwhitewashed fence, and sat down on a tree-box discouraged. Jim came skipping out at the gate with a tin pail, and singing "Buffalo Gals." Bringing water from the town pump had always been hateful work in Tom's eyes, before, but now it did not strike him so. He remembered that there was company at the pump. White, mulatto, and negro boys and girls were always there waiting their turns, resting, trading playthings, quarrelling, fighting, skylarking. And he remembered that although the pump was only a hundred and fifty yards off, Jim never got back with a bucket of water under an hour—and even then somebody generally had to go after him. Tom said:

"Say, Jim, I'll fetch the water if you'll whitewash some."

Jim shook his head and said:

"Can't, Mars Tom. Ole missis, she tole me I got to go an' git dis water an' not stop foolin' roun' wid anybody. She say she spec' Mars Tom gwine to ax me to whitewash, an' so she tole me go 'long an' 'tend to my own business—she 'lowed *she'd* 'tend to de whitewashin'."

"Oh, never you mind what she said, Jim. That's the way she always talks. Gimme the bucket—I won't be gone only a minute. *She* won't ever know."

"Oh, I dasn't, Mars Tom. Ole missis she'd take an' tar de head off 'n me. 'Deed she would."

"*She!* She never licks anybody—whacks 'em over the head with her thimble—and who cares for that, I'd like to know. She talks awful, but talk don't hurt—anyways it don't if she don't cry. Jim, I'll give you a marvel. I'll give you a white alley!"

Jim began to waver.

"White alley, Jim! And it's a bully taw."

"My! Dat's a mighty gay marvel, I tell you! But Mars Tom I's powerful 'fraid ole missis—"

"And besides, if you will I'll show you my sore toe."

Jim was only human—this attraction was too much for him. He put down his pail, took the white alley, and bent over the toe with absorbing interest while the bandage was being unwound. In another moment he was flying down the street with his pail and a tingling rear, Tom was whitewashing with vigor, and Aunt Polly was retiring from the field with a slipper in her hand and triumph in her eye.

But Tom's energy did not last. He began to think of the fun he had planned for this day, and his sorrows multiplied. Soon the free boys would come tripping along on all sorts of delicious expeditions, and they would make a world of fun of him for having to work—the very thought of it burnt him like fire. He got out his worldly wealth and examined it—bits of toys, marbles, and trash; enough to buy an exchange of work, maybe, but not half enough to buy so much as half an hour of pure freedom. So he returned his straitened means to his pocket, and gave up the idea of trying to buy the boys. At this dark and hopeless moment an inspiration burst upon him! Nothing less than a great, magnificent inspiration.

He took up his brush and went tranquilly to work. Ben Rogers hove in sight presently—the very boy, of all boys, whose ridicule he had been dreading. Ben's gait was the hop-skip-and-jump—proof enough that his heart was light and his anticipations high. He was eating an apple, and giving a long, melodious whoop, at intervals, followed by a deep-toned ding-dong-dong, ding-dong-dong, for he was personating a steamboat. As he drew near, he slackened speed, took the middle of the street, leaned far over to starboard and rounded to ponderously and with laborious pomp and circumstance—for he was personating the *Big Missouri*, and considered himself to be drawing nine feet of water. He was boat and captain and engine-bells combined, so he had to imagine himself standing on his own hurricane-deck giving the orders and executing them:

"Stop her, sir! Ting-a-ling-ling!" The headway ran almost out, and he drew up slowly toward the sidewalk.

"Ship up to back! Ting-a-ling-ling!" His arms straightened and stiffened down his sides.

"Set her back on the stabboard! Ting-a-ling-ling! Chow! ch-chow-wow! Chow!" His right hand, mean-time, describing stately circles—for it was representing a forty-foot wheel.

"Let her go back on the labboard! Ting-a-ling-ling! Chow-ch-chow-chow!" The left hand began to describe circles.

"Stop the stabboard! Ting-a-ling-ling! Stop the labboard! Come ahead on the stabboard! Stop her! Let your outside turn over slow! Ting-a-ling-ling! Chow-ow-ow! Get out that head-line! *Lively* now! Come—out with your spring-line—what're you about there! Take a turn round that stump with the bight of it! Stand by that stage, now—let her go! Done with the engines, sir! Ting-a-ling-ling! *Sh't! sh't! sh't!*" (trying the gauge-cocks).

Tom went on whitewashing—paid no attention to the steamboat. Ben stared a moment and then said: "Hi-*yi! You're* up a stump, ain't you!"

No answer. Tom surveyed his last touch with the eye of an artist, then he gave his brush another gentle sweep and surveyed the result, as before. Ben ranged up alongside of him. Tom's mouth watered for the apple, but he stuck to his work. Ben said:

"Hello, old chap, you got to work, hey?"

Tom wheeled suddenly and said:

"Why, it's you, Ben! I warn't noticing."

"Say—*I'm* going in a-swimming, *I* am. Don't you wish you could? But of course you'd druther *work*—wouldn't you? Course you would!"

Tom contemplated the boy a bit, and said:

"Why, ain't *that* work?" Illustrated by True Williams for Mark Twain in *The Adventures of Tom Sawyer* (Hartford, CT; Chicago; Cincinnati: The American Publishing Company, 1876).

"What do you call work?"

"Why, ain't *that* work?"

Tom resumed his whitewashing, and answered carelessly:

"Well, maybe it is, and maybe it ain't. All I know, is, it suits Tom Sawyer."

"Oh come, now, you don't mean to let on that you *like* it?"

The brush continued to move.

"Like it? Well, I don't see why I oughtn't to like it. Does a boy get a chance to whitewash a fence every day?"

That put the thing in a new light. Ben stopped nibbling his apple. Tom swept his brush daintily back and forth—stepped back to note the effect—added a touch here and there—criticised the effect again—Ben watching every move and getting more and more interested, more and more absorbed. Presently he said:

"Say, Tom, let *me* whitewash a little."

Tom considered, was about to consent; but he altered his mind:

"No—no—I reckon it wouldn't hardly do, Ben. You see, Aunt Polly's awful particular about this fence—right here on the street, you know—but if it was the back fence I wouldn't mind and she wouldn't. Yes, she's awful particular about this fence; it's got to be done very careful; I reckon there ain't one boy in a thousand, maybe two thousand, that can do it the way it's got to be done."

"No—is that so? Oh come, now—lemme just try. Only just a little—I'd let *you*, if you was me, Tom."

"Ben, I'd like to, honest injun; but Aunt Polly—well, Jim wanted to do it, but she wouldn't let him; Sid wanted to do it, and she wouldn't let Sid. Now don't you see how I'm fixed? If you was to tackle this fence and anything was to happen to it—"

"Oh, shucks, I'll be just as careful. Now lemme try. Say—I'll give you the core of my apple."

"Well, here—No, Ben, now don't. I'm afeard—"

"I'll give you *all* of it!"

Tom gave up the brush with reluctance in his face, but alacrity in his heart. And while the late steamer *Big Missouri* worked and sweated in the sun, the retired artist sat on a barrel in the shade close by, dangled his legs, munched his apple, and planned the slaughter of more innocents. There was no lack of material; boys happened along every little while; they came to jeer, but remained to whitewash. By the time Ben was fagged out, Tom had traded the next chance to Billy Fisher for a kite, in good repair; and when he played out, Johnny Miller bought in for a dead rat and a string to swing it with—and so on, and so on, hour after hour. And when the middle of the afternoon came, from being a poor poverty-stricken boy in the morning, Tom was literally rolling in wealth. He had besides the things before mentioned, twelve marbles, part of a jews'-harp, a piece of blue bottle-glass to look through, a spool cannon, a key that wouldn't unlock anything, a fragment of chalk, a glass stopper of a decanter, a tin soldier, a couple of tadpoles, six fire-crackers, a kitten with only one eye, a brass door-knob, a dog-collar—but no dog—the handle of a knife, four pieces of orange-peel, and a dilapidated old window-sash.

He had had a nice, good, idle time all the while—plenty of company—and the fence had three coats of whitewash on it! If he hadn't run out of whitewash he would have bankrupted every boy in the village.

Tom said to himself that it was not such a hollow world, after all. He had discovered a great law of human action, without knowing it—namely, that in order to make a man or a boy covet a thing, it is only necessary to make the thing difficult to attain. If he had been a great and wise philosopher, like the writer of this book, he would now have comprehended that Work consists of whatever a body is *obliged* to do, and that Play consists of whatever a body is not obliged to do. And this would help him to understand why constructing artificial flowers or performing on a tread-mill is work, while rolling ten-pins or climbing Mont Blanc is only amusement. There are wealthy gentlemen in England who drive four-horse passenger-coaches twenty or thirty miles on a daily line, in the summer, because the privilege costs them considerable money; but if they were offered wages for the service, that would turn it into work and then they would resign.

The boy mused awhile over the substantial change which had taken place in his worldly circumstances, and then wended toward headquarters to report.

Week Seventeen:
CASEY JONES

Come all you rounders if
   you want to hear
A story 'bout a brave engineer;
Casey Jones was the rounder's
   name
"Twas on the Illinois Central
   that he won his fame.

Casey Jones, he loved a
   locomotive.
Casey Jones, a mighty man was
   he.
Casey Jones run his final
   locomotive
With the Cannonball Special on
   the old I. C.

Casey pulled into Memphis on
   Number Four,
The engine foreman met him at
   the roundhouse door;
Said, "Joe Lewis won't be able to
   make his run
So you'll have to double out on
   Number One."

If I can have Sim Webb, my
   fireman, my engine 382,
Although I'm tired and weary,
   I'll take her through.
Put on my whistle that come in
   today
Cause I mean to keep her
   wailing as we ride and pray.

Casey Jones, mounted the cabin,
Casey Jones, with the orders in
   his hand.
Casey Jones, he mounted the
   cabin,
Started on his farewell Journey
   to the promised land.

They pulled out of Memphis
   nearly two hours late,
Soon they were speeding at a
   terrible rate.
And the people knew by the
   whistle's moan.
That the man at the throttle was
   Casey Jones.

Need more coal there, fireman
　Sim,
Open that door and heave it in.
Give that shovel all you got
And we'll reach Canton on the
　dot.

On April 30, 1900, that rainy
　morn,
Down in Mississippi near the
　town of Vaughan,
Sped the Cannonball Special
　only two minutes late
Traveling 70 miles an hour
　when they saw a freight.

The caboose number 83 was on
　the main line,
Casey's last words were "Jump,
　Sim, while you have the time.
"At 3:52 that morning came the
　fareful end,
Casey took his farewell trip to
　the promised land.

Casey Jones, he died at the
　throttle,
With the whistle in his hand.
Casey Jones, he died at the
　throttle,
But we'll all see Casey in the
　promised land.

His wife and three children were
　left to mourn
The tragic death of Casey on
　that April morn.
May God through His goodness
　keep them by His grace
Till they all meet together in
　that heavenly place.

Casey's body lies buried in
　Jackson, Tennessee
Close beside the tracks of the
　old I. C.
May his spirit live forever
　throughout the land
As the greatest of all heroes of a
　railroad man.

Casey Jones, he died at the
　throttle,
Casey Jones, with the whistle in
　his hand.
Casey Jones, he died at the
　throttle,
But we'll all see Casey in the
　promised land.
　　WALLACE SAUNDERS
　(c. late 1800s–early 1900s)

Week Eighteen

Joe Mufferaw

Canadian Tall Tale

TRANSLATED AND ADAPTED BY JENNIFER COURTNEY

Big Joseph Montferrand, afterward known as Joe Mufferaw, was born in Montreal, Canada in October of 1802. He was the sweetest, most pious, and most modest of all his classmates. His sister inspired in him a great trust in God. One would hardly have believed that he would become such a renowned fighter that his fame would spread to all of North America.

Joe had a great sense of justice and would never tolerate the older and stronger children in his neighborhood to mistreat the younger and smaller ones. At school, he appointed himself the protector of the small pupils. His motto was "Use force with the powerful; show mercy to the weak."

One day when he was very young, he moved an enormous piece of wood, the size of a full-grown tree trunk, all by himself. His mother believed in keeping him humble. She said, "Pshaw, you are strong, but it's not that glorious. Your father was stronger than you."

When fighting Joe was just six years old, he was digging a hole at the front of his father's property. A grown man called Michel Duranleau crossed the street with two other giant bullies. He knocked Joe down to the ground. At this insult, Joe coiled up like a spring, sprang from the earth, and landed in the middle of the men. Duranleau had never lost before. He and his two friends fled the country.

In his youth, Joe didn't walk on the earth, instead, he left boot marks on the ceilings of all the houses. His favorite pastime was leaping over tables and walls.

Even though he was huge and powerful, he kept a sweet disposition. He was very careful of his superhuman strength. In those days, the English brought the sport of boxing to Canada and made it popular. Fights were always breaking out in the streets, especially at the times of elections.

One day, when Joe was just 16, two famous English boxers had a fight in Montreal, and one was declared the winner. Unafraid, Joe jumped into the ring and crowed like a rooster which meant that he wanted to challenge the champion. They said he knocked on the champion like a scythe against a sheaf of wheat. Still, he remained modest.

As an adult, Joe began to work in the fur and lumber industries throughout Canada. His fame continued to spread. He was well-known for his long, strong arms, his legs which kicked like a snapping whip, and the incredible flexibility of his whole body. His courage and composure in a fight were truly frightening. Most of the time, he did not have to work hard in a fight, but in the case of defending someone's honor, he was a sight to see!

In addition to being quick with his fists, Joe was quick with his words. Once, Joe fought a man called Berlinguet. Their fight started with a battle of words.

Joe, "No one is brave enough to face me!"

Berlinguet, "I think you neither believe in God nor in the devil."

Joe, "I believe in God; as to the devil, he lives in man, bring him to me in his natural costume, and I will strangle him!"

Both Joe and his brother Louis were huge men about six and a half feet tall. For a time, they worked clearing the forests together. Once, Louis cut and stacked five cords of wood in one night. That would make a pile twenty feet high by forty feet wide by twenty feet deep! The villagers were so impressed that they doubled his salary.

Joe and Louis always took care of the poor and mistreated. They were champions of widows and orphans. If a poor carter (one who hired himself to transport goods with his horse and cart) lost his animal, Joe and Louis raised the money to replace it.

In 1828, in Quebec, Montferrand was a lodger at the Hotel Quebec. One day, an English naval captain introduced himself to Joe.

"I have come to you," said one captain, "to see if you would fight against the champion of the English navy."

These words had scarcely been loosed when Montferrand told him: "I accept!" His patriotism never hesitated. The two met near the dock of the queen. One trait that illustrates the values of the times, is that many women joined the crowd to watch the fight. The soldiers of the garrison had to form a chain in order to contain the two thousand spectators of that scene. Many bets were made. Montferrand ignored this circumstance and prepared for the fight.

The English champion was a colossus of six feet four inches in height. His torso and his arms were covered in hair. His appearance would have been imposing to the bravest—so that Joe thought himself lost. A general shudder went through his body. He did not know which way to turn.

All at once, the regimental band struck up some music. This had a magical effect on our hero. He entered in the circle and placed himself on guard. The Englishman had a skillful punch, which he believed irresistible, but he was wrong. The crowd applauded. Suddenly, the confidence of the onlookers took up Joe's cause. The Englishman now doubted the bottomless force which he believed himself to possess. At the second round, the stranger gave signs of weakness, and at that moment, all signs pointed in favor of the Canadian. At the seventh round, a clever feint allowed Joe to hit the English sailor on the head, close to his eye. Trying not to be excessive, at the seventeenth round, Joe launched two punches that knocked his adversary out of the fight.

The captain and many others in the crowd who loved this barbaric sport, shook Joe's hand forcefully and gave him two thousand coins, forming a part of the winnings.

"I want," said Joe, "to keep the title of champion of the five parts of the world that you have given me; as to the money, give it to the poor devil that I have beaten. He needs it more than I do. He will have to rehabilitate his poor carcass. I do not fight for money."

The captain replied, "Well, come with me, I would like to travel around the word with you as my good friend. To begin, let us dine together."

"I will dine with you, but we will go no farther together. You know I am not attached to money; it would cost me too much to leave my country!"

Now, it is well known that Bill Collins had the reputation of being one of the best boxers in Montreal and the supplest of those who use foot and fist. It was his habit to wander the neighborhood of Saint-Laurent, making threats with his mouth, designating his victims in advance.

All about town, he crowed like a rooster. He was in league with Edward Perreault and Louis Picard. They knew Joe, and they invited him to meet with Collins on their turf in a fair fight. Joe saw, upon entering, a large fire which burned in the chimney, and on the other side of the room, a buffet. They served a round of drinks. Collins, hidden under the bar, stood so suddenly that he broke the glass from which Joe drank. In a flash, Joe leaned over the counter, seized Collins, and threw him into the chimney, where he was grilled a little until his friends pulled him out. He did not ask to finish the fight. This put an end to many of the boasting men who went around imitating Collins.

Canadian foresters, who spread far and wide up the Ottawa River, made the village of Bytown their headquarters. The Chaudière canyon interrupted navigation and meant that any travelers must cross by bridge. This bridge is the scene of one of Joe's best exploits.

One day, in 1820, more than one hundred and fifty men had ambushed Hull at the end of the bridge. Joe went to cross and see what was going on. The enemy rushed to meet him. Joe wanted to flee, but the woman had closed the bridge door. The men waved clubs and uttered threats. Joe made quick strides to get closer to the attackers.

One of them fell into Joe's hands. Joe seized him by the feet and laid him out on the ground. Then, continuing to pick the men up like rag dolls, he threw them to the right and to the left into the white foam of the river.

At the time of the attack, Joe had prayed to the Blessed Virgin and made the sign of the cross. One of the tumbled fighters got up on one knee. Just at the moment when the formidable grip of Joe the giant was going to make him suffer the fate of others, this man made the sign of the cross. "Get behind me," Joe commanded the man. Then, without delay, he sprang forward again, and renewed the attack. The remaining men took flight and Joe crossed the bridge in the same way he walked everywhere, as a champion.

With his big blue eyes, his dark blond hair, his fair complexion, and his rosy cheeks, when Joe entered a ball, everyone had eyes only for him. He was an incomparable dancer. At the table, he was all gaiety and good manners, in the fashion of the old lords.

Joe never went anywhere without being gallant. In the city as in the village, his evenings belonged to the ladies. With his jovial spirit, his impeccable manners, his innate politeness, and his reputation as an invincible fighter, he was irresistible. He captivated all hearts, attracted all eyes, and ruled all the circles he traveled in. He inspired a thousand loving glances, but this Adonis took it all in stride.

Once, he visited a small, well-kept hotel which had changed ownership. He confessed that he did not have any money and made to leave. The woman behind the counter told him to stay and have a drink. Before leaving, he thanked the woman for her kindness. He then placed himself in the middle of the room and marked the ceiling with the nails of his boot: "Here, madame, a business card. You can show it to your customers. My name is Joe Mufferaw." In later years, people came from miles around to see his signature, and the hotel became famous.

One day, a regiment was exercising on a square in Montreal. They had just lined up when Joe passed by. The soldiers pointed him out to each other; in an instant all discipline was forgotten. At first, the officers were dismayed by the lack of discipline. Then, the superior officers saw Joe. This explained everything, and the soldiers were forgiven by their leaders!

Joe was an accomplished swimmer. Once, the Irish gangs searched for him to take revenge over the Hull Bridge affair. One day, he was surprised by a group that surrounded him. He had to swim across the river. On the opposite shore, another band, armed with rifles, was lying in wait for him. He jumped off the waterfall, uttering a fervent prayer to heaven. Two hours later, everyone believed that Joe was engulfed in the Ottawa, but he was really quietly changing his clothes at a hotel.

As time went on, it came to pass that Joe realized he had grown old. He could not believe that he was 54! He began to prepare to sink into a beautiful old age. He walked the streets daily, his head held high, visiting with all he met, finally enjoying life. His beautiful face shone under the gazes of all the eyes that followed him. He would visit the butcher who cheered and joked with him. Then, he would walk among the farmers' carts, teasing the women, jeering at the men, and greeting everyone happily.

When he straightened up and spoke animatedly, he was still the handsome boy of 1830, without boastfulness, without ostentation, with all his heart and generous movements. "Oh! he said sometimes, the more I reflect, the more I realize that I have been a great wretch; I repent; May God forgive me the miseries of a life that I have found so long useless and often harmful!"

Joe died in 1864. He had the beautiful privilege of being loved by all who knew him. You would be mistaken if you remembered him as a rude Hercules, always eager for a fight. Many people imagine this formidable athlete fearing neither God nor devil, but nothing could be further from the truth. Whenever he found himself in danger, he prayed for courage.

His comrades, who were proud of him, had reprimanded him quite a few times for not entering a fight. To this he replied:

"I promised my mother and the Blessed Virgin to act only if I saw something bad, a wrong, an unmerited insult, or the strong oppressing the weak."

Indeed, we cannot blame him for showing his strength and valor. There was a deep fund of chivalry in his heart and in his imagination. In the Middle Ages, he would have carried the spear with splendor, for God, his lady, and his king.

Fin (French for "The End")

Week Eighteen

CROOKED MICK
Australian Tall Tale

COMPILED AND EMBELLISHED BY JENNIFER COURTNEY

You have probably heard some tall tales about a fellow called Pecos Bill or another one called Paul Bunyan. You have maybe even heard tell of a man called Joe Mufferaw from up in Canada. Some call these men giants and tell the most amazing lies about them. They don't have anything on the biggest man from the farthest points of Australia, a fellow known as Crooked Mick. He was the biggest, fastest, and strongest of them all.

Crooked Mick could shear 500 sheep a day without batting an eyelash or feeling tired. He could stare down a kangaroo the size of a bull elephant, and he could eat enough meat pies in a meal to bankrupt the whole country.

One time, when Mick was a young man, he came upon a depressed looking man whose wagon and team had disappeared into a bog. Mick ripped out a sapling by its roots and used it as a lever to push that team and wagon out of the bog. As they raced up out of that mucky mess and tore off, they dumped their load of sugar into the creek. It has been known as Sweetwater Creek ever since.

Folks tell different stories about how Mick came to be known as Crooked Mick, but I know that it happened this way. One day, Mick was crossing a river when the water level was low. Mick had his team of 100 bullocks pulling his wagon. With his reputation, he would drive no smaller team. When they made it to the middle of the river, they bogged down in the mud. Nevertheless, he drove his team ahead. It took an awfully long time. When they finally made it to the other side, they found that they had pulled a bend in the river by driving that big team through. Ever since that day, he has been known as Crooked Mick.

Crooked Mick could often be found working in the Speewah Station, the biggest sheep-shearing station in all of Australia. On this station lived about five million sheep. More than 10,000 men worked at this sheep station, most of the time in the shearing shed which was a mere 14 miles long. As a matter of fact, everything was bigger on the Speewah Station. The mud was deeper and stickier, the men were taller and hungrier, the droughts were longer, hotter, and drier, and the kangaroos were taller than Mount Kosciuszko itself. Although the Speewah enjoyed these epic proportions, no one quite knows where to find it. Perhaps, if you travel to Australia, and you keep traveling west across that country, you will be the first to find it again.

The Speewah is a place of dangers and wonders, so you have to watch your step at all times. There are holes in the earth that will swallow up dogs, men, wagons, and cattle. There are strange creatures such as two-headed emus, flying snakes, centipedes twenty feet long, and even the dreaded bunyip. The bunyip is a creature known only to Australia. It has the face of a dingo, the body of a crocodile, the flippers of a fish, the tail of a horse, and two massive tusks like a walrus.

The owner of the Speewah Station had a daughter who fell ill. He sent Mick to fetch her some medicine. Mick took this task rather seriously. In just three hours, he rode from sunrise to sunset. And that's how he was promoted to manager of the station.

On this speedy journey, it did not hurt that Mick was riding his trusty horse The Speewah Rebel. No other horse could beat his horse in a race. His horse was so wild that he once bucked Mick high enough to see the eggs in a nest 15 feet from the ground. Another time, that wild horse bucked so hard that he moved his own brand from his shoulder to a spot just under his ear.

Even though they were powerfully huge birds, the crows on the Speewah station were unable to break the shells of the eggs laid by the giant emus. So, they fetched large stones, flew up into the air with them, and dropped them down on those eggs right in the nests. The cattle dogs on the Speewah Station were so fierce that they could bite a cow twice on the heel without ever letting go their grip.

There was a bunyip on the station that made daily trips to a hollowed-out stump. Mick determined to catch it as a way of making his fortune. He had escaped from a bunyip once before by climbing a tall tree. Just before the bunyip caught up to him, Mick remembered that those infernal animals could climb trees, so he reached down and pulled up the tree trunk after himself.

One morning, Mick watched carefully as the bunyip shimmied backward down that favorite hollowed-out stump to return to his home in the swamp. Once more, he contemplated the best way to catch this monster. Since that beast took all the trouble to leave the swamp and visit that stump every single day, Mick figured that there must be something important in that stump. He sat his giant self down on a giant rock that was actually a mountain and began to think. After a powerfully long and deep think, he sprang to his feet and shouted, "I've got it!" He jumped so hard that he cracked the earth into a canyon that ran the whole length of the Speewah Station. He shouted so loud, that his echo resounded through the sheep station for a full week.

What Mick had gotten was this. The bunyip must have concealed her young offspring in that tree trunk for safe keeping. Mick's plan was to catch that young bunyip and travel around the country charging for folks to look at it. His plans for making a fortune were sure! One day, Mick tied up his horse and then climbed up that tree stump with a wool sack in his hands to pop over that head of that young bunyip. He peered down in the hollow trunk and had to stuff his fist down his throat to quiet his cry of joy. For, you see, he had seen two beady eyes glistening down in that tree trunk, and he knew he had been right.

Carefully and cautiously, he made his way down inside that stump. His clothes were almost torn off, and along with them his arms and his legs, but he stayed focused on his mission. Finally, he reached the owner of those glistening, beady eyes and popped the wool sack over its head. Then, too late, he realized his mistake. Oh, yes, he was in a mighty terrible predicament. The inside of the tree was too slippery for him to climb back out with his prize.

Mick tried and tried to climb out. He tried to cut notches in the trunk with his knife, but the wood was too hard. His horse got himself loose from his rope and took off for home, so he was no help. Mick's only hope was to wait for the nightly visit of the mother bunyip. Sure enough, just after sunset, she climbed into that hollow tree to visit her young one. As she got close to Mick, he slipped a rope around her neck and pulled it tight. She was so surprised that she gave out a furious growl and then launched herself out of that hollow tree, pulling Mick behind her. They shot out of that tree like a couple of cannon balls. The mother bunyip landed a few hundred yards away from Mick. The wool sack holding her young one landed beside her and flew open. The mother quickly snatched her baby and lumbered away for the safety of the swamp. Mick headed home with no bunyip and no way of making his fortune. So, he kept on shearing the sheep at the station until he reached a ripe old age and died. He will never be forgotten, though, as long as you keep telling his story.

Week Eighteen:

O Captain! My Captain!

O Captain! my Captain! our fearful trip is done;
The ship has weather'd every rack, the prize we sought is won;
The port is near, the bells I hear, the people all exulting,
While follow eyes the steady keel, the vessel grim and daring:
But O heart! heart! heart!
O the bleeding drops of red,
Where on the deck my Captain lies,
Fallen cold and dead!

O Captain! my Captain! rise up and hear the bells;
Rise up—for you the flag is flung—for you the bugle trills;
For you bouquets and ribbon'd wreaths—for you the shores
a-crowding;
For you they call, the swaying mass, their eager faces turning;
Here Captain! dear father!
This arm beneath your head;
It is some dream that on the deck
You've fallen cold and dead.

My Captain does not answer, his lips are pale and still;
My father does not feel my arm, he has no pulse nor will.
The ship is anchor'd safe and sound, its voyage closed and done;
From fearful trip the victor ship comes in with object won:
   Exult, O shores, and ring, O bells!
     But I, with mournful tread,
       Walk the deck my Captain lies,
         Fallen cold and dead.

WALT WHITMAN
(1819–1892)

"O Captain! My Captain!" Illustration by N. C. Wyeth in *Poems of American Patriotism*, edited by Brander Matthews (New York: C. Scribner's Sons, 1923).

Week Nineteen:

WHY THE TIGER AND THE STAG FEAR EACH OTHER

Brazilian Folk Tale

RETOLD BY ELSIE SPICER EELLS

Once upon a time there was a large handsome stag with great branching horns. One day he said to himself, "I am tired of having no home of my own, and of just living anywhere. I shall build me a house." He searched on every hill, in every valley, by every stream, and under all the trees for a suitable place. At last he found one that was just right. It was not too high, nor too low, not too near a stream and not too far away from one, not under too thick trees and not away from the trees out under the hot sun. "I am going to build my house here," he said, and he began to clear a place for it at once. He worked all day and did not go away until night.

Now in that same country there lived a large handsome tiger, with sharp, sharp teeth and bright, cruel eyes. One day the tiger said to himself, "I am tired of having no home of my own,—of just living around anywhere! I shall build me a house." Accordingly the tiger searched for a place to build his house. He searched on every hill, in every valley, by every stream, and under all the trees. At last he found a place which was just right. It was not too high nor too low, not too near a stream and not too far away from one, not under too thick trees and yet not away from the trees out in the hot sun. The tiger said to himself, "I am going to build my house here. The place is all ready for me for there isn't very much underbrush here." He began at once and finished clearing the place. Then it became daylight and he went away.

At daylight the stag came back to do more work on his new house. "H'm," he said when he looked at the clearing. "Somebody is helping me. The place is cleared and ready for me to build the foundation."

He began to work at once and worked all day. At night when the foundation was laid, he went away.

At night the tiger came to work at his new house. "H'm," he said when he looked at it. "Somebody is helping me. The foundations of my house are all laid." He began to work at once and built the sides of the house. He worked all night and went away at daybreak, leaving the house with the sides completed. There was a big door and a funny little window in the side.

At daybreak the stag came back to work on his house. When he saw it he rubbed his eyes for he thought that he must be dreaming. The sides of the house were completed with a big door and a funny little window. "Somebody must surely be helping me," he said to himself as he began to work to put on the roof. He worked hard all day and when the sun went down, there was a roof of dried grass on the house. "I can sleep in my own house to-night," he said. He made his bed in the corner and soon was sound asleep.

At night the tiger came back to work on his new house. When he saw it he rubbed his eyes for he thought that he must be dreaming. There was a roof of dried grass on the house.

"Somebody must surely be helping me," he said to himself as he entered the door. The first thing he saw when he entered the door was the stag sound asleep in his bed in the corner. "Who are you and what are you doing in my house?" he said in his deepest voice.

The stag woke up with a start. "Who are you and what are you doing in my house?" said the stag in his deepest voice.

"It is not your house. It is mine. I built it myself," said the tiger.

"It is my house," said the stag. "I built it myself."

"I made the clearing for the house," said the tiger, "I built the sides and made the door and window."

"I started the clearing," said the stag. "I laid the foundations and put on the roof of dried grass."

The stag and the tiger quarrelled all night about whose house it was. At day-break they decided that they would live together there.

The next night the tiger said to the stag, "I'm going hunting. Get the water and have the wood ready for the fire. I shall be almost famished when I return."

The stag got the wood and water ready. After a while the tiger came back. He brought home for dinner a great handsome stag. The stag had no appetite at all and he didn't sleep a wink that night.

The next day the stag said that he was going hunting. He told the tiger to have the wood and water ready when he got back. The tiger got the wood and water ready. By and by the stag came back bringing with him the body of a great tiger.

"I am nearly famished," said the stag. "Let's have dinner right away." The tiger hadn't any appetite at all and he could not eat a mouthful.

That night neither the tiger nor the stag could sleep a wink. The tiger was afraid the stag would kill him if he shut his eyes for a minute, and the stag was afraid the tiger would kill him if he slept or even pretended to be asleep. Accordingly he kept wide awake too.

Toward morning the stag got very cramped from keeping in one position so long. He moved his head slightly. In doing this his horns struck against the roof of the house. It made a terrible noise. The tiger thought that the stag was about to spring upon him and kill him. He made a leap for the door and ran out of it as fast as he could. He ran and ran until he was far, far away from the house with the roof of dried grass.

The stag thought that the tiger was about to spring upon him and kill him. He, too, made a leap for the door and ran and ran until he was far, far away from the house with the roof of dried grass. The tiger and the stag are still running away from each other until this very day. The house with the roof of dried grass waited and waited there in the place which was neither too high nor too low, too near the river nor too far away, not under too thick trees nor out in the hot sun. It waited and waited until it go so tired it fell down in a heap.

"The falcon flew towards the earth with the violin." Illustrated by Helen M. Barton for Ellie Spicer Eells in *Fairy Tales from Brazil: How and Why Stories from Brazilian Folk-Lore* (New York: Dodd, Mead & Co., 1917).

Week Nineteen:

How the Toad Got His Bruises

Brazilian Folk Tale

RETOLD BY ELSIE SPICER EELLS

Once upon a time, ages and ages ago, the toad had a smooth skin. In those days he was a great gad about. He never could be found in his own house. If any one had a party he was sure to go, no matter how far away from home it was held, or how long it took to get there.

One day the toad received an invitation to attend a party in the sky. "You never can get to this party," said his friend, the armadillo. "You know how slowly you travel here upon earth."

"Wait and see whether or not I go to the party?" said the toad.

Not far from the toad's house there lived a big black buzzard. No one liked the buzzard. He was very unpopular with all the birds and beasts. The toad hopped over to the buzzard's house. The buzzard was outside the door making music on his violin.

"Good morning, Friend Buzzard," said the toad. "Are you going to attend the party in the sky?"

The buzzard replied that he was planning to go.

"That is good," said the toad. "May I have the pleasure of your company for the trip?"

The buzzard was delighted to have the toad seek his company. It was a new experience.

"I'll be charmed to go to the party with you," replied the buzzard. "What time shall we start?"

"We'll start at four o'clock," said the toad. "Come to my house and we'll go on from there. Be sure to bring your violin with you."

Promptly at four o'clock the buzzard arrived at the toad's house. He had his violin with him, of course, because the toad had asked him to bring it.

"I'm not quite ready to go," the toad called out. "Just leave your violin there by the door and step inside. It will take me only a minute to finish my toilet."

The buzzard laid his violin carefully outside the door and went inside the toad's house. The toad jumped through the window and hid himself inside the violin.

The buzzard waited and waited for the toad to get ready but he did not hear a word from the toad. Finally he got tired of waiting. He picked up his violin and started.

When he arrived at the party he was a trifle late but he explained how he had waited for the toad.

"How foolish to wait a minute for the toad," said his hosts. "How could the toad ever get to a party in the sky? We just asked him as a joke because he is such a great gad about. Lay down your violin and come to the feast."

The buzzard laid down his violin. As soon as there was no one looking, out hopped the toad. He was laughing from ear to ear. "So they thought I would not come to the party! What a joke! How surprised they will be to see me here!" he said.

There was nobody at the feast who was as gay as the toad. When the buzzard asked how he arrived he said: "I'll tell you some other day." Then he went on eating and dancing.

The buzzard did not have a very good time at the party. He decided that he would go home early. He went away without saying good-bye to his hosts and without taking his violin with him.

At the end of the party the toad hopped inside the violin and waited and waited for the buzzard to take him home. Nobody picked up the violin and the toad began to be very much worried. He almost wished he had not come.

After a while the falcon noticed the violin. "That violin belongs to the buzzard. He must have forgotten to take it home. I'll carry it back for him," he said.

The falcon flew towards earth with the violin. The toad shook about terribly inside of the violin. He got very tired. The falcon got tired, too.

"I'm not going to carry this heavy old violin of the buzzard's another minute," said the falcon. "I was foolish to offer to carry it in the first place. The buzzard is no friend of mine."

He let the violin fall. Down, down toward earth it fell.

"O, little stones, O, little stones, get out of my way," called the toad as he fell. The little stones had deaf ears. They did not get out of the way.

When the toad crawled out of the wrecked violin he was so covered with bruises that he could hardly hop home.

The buzzard never knew what became of his violin or why the toad had lost his good looks. To this very day the toad shows his bruises. And he is entirely cured of being a gad about.

Cattle in Pasture—Sunset, Nantucket (detail, c. 1883) by American artist George Inness. San

Week Nineteen:

AN EVENING AT THE FARM

Over the hill the farm-boy goes.
His shadow lengthens along the land,
A giant staff in a giant hand;
In the poplar tree, above the spring,
The katydid begins to sing;
　The early dews are falling;—
Into the stone-heap darts the mink;
The swallows skim the river's brink;
And home to the woodland fly the crows,
When over the hill the farm-boy goes,
　Cheerily calling,
　"Co', boss! co', boss! co'! co'! co'!"
Farther, farther, over the hill,
Faintly calling, calling still,
　"Co', boss! co', boss! co'! co'!"

Into the yard the farmer goes,
With grateful heart, at the close of day:
Harness and chain are hung away;
In the wagon-shed stand yoke and plough,
The straw's in the stack, the hay in the mow,
　The cooling dews are falling;—
The friendly sheep his welcome bleat,
The pigs come grunting to his feet,
And the whinnying mare her master knows,
When into the yard the farmer goes,
　His cattle calling,—
　"Co', boss! co', boss! co'! co'! co'!"
While still the cow-boy, far away,
Goes seeking those that have gone astray,—
　"Co', boss! co', boss! co'! co'!"

Now to her task the milkmaid
    goes.
The cattle come crowding
    through the gate,
Lowing, pushing, little and
    great;
About the trough, by the
    farm-yard pump,
The frolicsome yearlings frisk
    and jump,
    While the pleasant dews are
      falling;—
The new milch-heifer is quick
    and shy,
But the old cow waits with
    tranquil eye,
And the white stream into the
    blight pail flows,
When to her task the milkmaid
    goes,
    Soothingly calling,
    "So, boss! so, boss! so! so! so!"
The cheerful milkmaid takes her
    stool,
And sits and milks in the
    twilight cool,
    Saying "So! so, boss! so! so!"

To supper at last the farmer
    goes.
The apples are pared, the paper
    read,
The stories are told, then all to
    bed.
Without, the crickets' ceaseless
    song
Makes shrill the silence all night
    long;
    The heavy dews are falling.
The housewife's hand has turned
    the lock;
Drowsily ticks the kitchen clock;
The household sinks to deep
    repose,
But still in sleep the farm-boy
    goes
    Singing, calling,—
    "Co', boss! co', boss! co'! co'!
    co'!"
And oft the milkmaid, in her
    dreams,
Drums in the pail with the
    flashing streams,
    Murmuring "So, boss! so!"

JOHN TOWNSEND TROWBRIDGE
(1827–1916)

Week Twenty:

FRANCISCO'S HOME

Argentinian Short Story

BY EVA CANNON BROOKS

Francisco sat crosslegged in one corner of the *patio* ["courtyard"] under the shade of a small pomegranate tree which grew in a tub. He had moved halfway around the *patio* since morning, trying to keep out of the sun. Just after *café* ["coffee"] he had started out under the shade of the east wall, where wistaria vines and jasmine grew in a dense mass of purple, yellow and green; then he had gone from one tubbed shelter to another as the sun mounted higher, until now only the heavy foliage of the pomegranate offered protection from the hot rays. All of the longvarnished blinds at the doors of the rooms opening upon this central, stone-paved courtyard, had long since been closed securely, for it was middle December and the house must be sealed early against the noon heat of midsummer.

Francisco might have gone inside, where the darkened rooms furnished some relief, but he chose to sit crosslegged on the red and white square stones of the *patio*, with his back to the main part of the house, so that the mother and sisters could not see what occupied his busy hands.

Francisco's father was dead, and he, with his mother, La Señora Anita Maria Lacevera de Gonzalez, and his two sisters, Elena Maria, who was six, and Guillerma Maria, who was eighteen and very beautiful, lived in the Calle Cerrito, in the city of Buenos Aires, Argentine Republic, South America.

Francisco, himself, was nine, and his uncle who was a colonel in the army and who supported his widowed sister and her family, expected him to be a soldier also. His great-grandfather had been a general, and because of his services during the revolution that had brought Argentina her liberty nearly one hundred years ago, his family was one of the most distinguished in the Republic. Francisco's own grandfather had given his life for his *patria* ["homeland"] during the ten years' blockade of Buenos Aires, when the French and English forces combined to overcome General Rosas, who then commanded the city. His mother and his uncle, the Colonel Juan Carlos Lacevera, were then little children, but they were fired with a patriotism that comes only to those who have given of their own flesh and blood for native land.

"El Coronel Lacevera" was now retired, and with his wife and six daughters lived in a spacious, palatial home in the Calle San Martin facing the beautiful plaza, or park, where the statue of General San Martin on his rearing charger stands, a constant reminder to the hundreds of little Argentine boys and girls who daily play in the pebbled space around it, of the wonderful man, who, like George Washington, was first in war, first in peace, and is still first in the hearts of his countrymen.

The monthly allowance bestowed by Colonel Lacevera upon his sister was enough to keep them in comfort, but not sufficient to allow them to live in luxury, and to-day, because Francisco had not enough money to buy his Christmas *pesebre* ["manger"] at the toyshop, he was doing what many little boys of that country do,—he was making his own.

Now, you must know right here, that Christmas in these South American countries is not the greatest festival of the entire year, as it is with us; it is simply one of the many that are celebrated at frequent intervals, for Argentina is a land of *fiestas* ["parties" or "holidays"]; there is scarcely a month that does not allow three or four holidays from school because of some *fiesta*, either of church or state. Although they do not celebrate this great holiday as we do with Christmas trees and visits from Santa Claus, they have something in their places, and it is the "Coming of the Three Kings." In anticipation of this, all over the Republic, children erect *pesebres* or mangers.

A *pesebre* consists of a miniature open shed, or merely a roof of straw or bark, underneath which, in a tiny box, lies a porcelain baby doll to represent the infant Christ. Bending in adoration at the head of the wee box that holds this image kneels the mother, Mary, and at the foot, with folded hands, stands Joseph, the father. About them, placed in sand or moss, that forms the floor of the stable or yard, are figures to represent the worshipful neighbours, also the farm-yard fowls and animals; cows and donkeys predominating. They look like Noah's Ark people, stiff-legged and prim. Now all of this remains unmoved, a spot of reverent adoration, throughout Christmas week, New Year's day, and until "twelfth night," or the fifth of January. It is awaiting the great event for which it was erected, the "Coming of the Three Kings."

On that auspicious night, through the same magical means that aid Santa Claus to enter the homes of North American children while their eyes are closed in sleep, come the three richly decorated and delicately carved kings on miniature camels with costly trappings and bags of spices on their little brown backs.

On the morning of the sixth of January the children awake, all eagerness to see the arrivals of the night. Rushing to the *pesebre* they find the three little wooden kings kneeling beside the manger, the faithful camels standing in the grass without, and all about on the floor are the wonderful gifts that the kings have brought to their *pesebre*. Indeed, as you can see, it was erected for just this purpose, exactly as the fir tree with its glittering ornaments forms the nucleus in other lands for Christmas gifts.

It was these wooden people and animals that Francisco's small fingers were fashioning. He had cut himself several times, and one finger was bound up in an old handkerchief, but his enthusiasm was not lessened because of it. He knew exactly how they should be carved, and how many there should be, for in the toyshop windows there had been sets of them on display for weeks, and Francisco had studied each necessary bit carefully.

In a box beside him were the finished product of his penknife. Joseph and Mary were completed even to the paint; Mary's red and blue gown and Joseph's yellow robe were not quite dry, and the cows were too vividly red, but that would not matter; Elena was no severe critic, and it was mainly for her that he was carving them. Elena had been ill and this was to be her "getting well" gift. The flashing light in her great brown eyes when she should see them would be sufficient reward for cut fingers and weary back. Besides, this was the summer vacation and there was nothing else to do.

In all countries on the other side of the Equator the seasons are the reverse of those on this side. In Argentina the children are having their summer holidays in December, January, and February, when the children of the Northern hemisphere are busy in school, or skating and sleighing; and they are having their winter when the Northern children are dressed in their thinnest clothing and are going away to the seashore or mountains.

Francisco had just completed a wonderful set of bent pin horns for one of the red cows when he was called to breakfast, and it was half-past eleven. But you see their meal hours, like their seasons, are different from ours. At eight o'clock he had had his *cafe con leche*, or coffee with hot milk, and a roll; at half-past eleven he was accustomed to having his breakfast; at four he would have *máte* or tea; and at seven dinner would be served.

Francisco gathered his treasures into the tin box, and hurried to the bath-room to make himself ready for *almuerzo* ["lunch"]. When he entered the dining-room his mother and Guillerma, the elder sister, were seated, and the little Indian serving-maid was arranging a tray to carry to Elena in the bed-room.

The meal consisted of beef broth and rice, called *caldo* and the usual beginning to every hearty meal in that country; then came fried fish with garlic, followed by a stew of mutton, carrots, cabbage, potatoes, and large pieces of yellow pumpkin, this being the native dish of the Argentines and commonly known as *puchero*. After that came fruit and coffee.

Guillerma chatted continuously of the wonderful new gowns which she had seen being packed at the great house in Calle San Martin, where she had been the day before, to bid her aunt and six cousins good-bye, before their departure for Mar-de-la-Plata, the fashionable watering place on the Atlantic Ocean, a day's ride by rail from Buenos Aires.

Meanwhile, as they sat thus, eating and talking, over in the great house of the *Coronel* ["Colonel"] the master sat at his massive library table playing solitaire. He always ended his meals thus with his after-dinner coffee-cup beside him. The walls were lined with well-filled bookcases, for the Colonel was a scholar.

Indeed, he cared little for the gay life that ebbed and flowed about him because of his high social position, and because of the six comely daughters, ranging from fourteen to twenty-four; the eldest ones of whom were favourites in exclusive Buenos Aires society. He suffered it because of his love for them, but his natural fondness for quiet and study led him to think longingly of the large estate in the Province of Santa Fé, where he could spend the remaining years of his life in the free open air, enjoying the quiet and solitude he so loved. But the daughters must be educated and their mother did not like the country, so the Colonel was forced to live through the winter months in the noise and roar of the great city; contenting himself with a few months each summer at the estate, when he rode at will over the wide prairies on his swift Argentine horse, or read for hours under the shade of the wide spreading *ombú* trees which surrounded the country house. This *estáncia*, as they term a very large farm or ranch, was really his wife's; in fact, so was the city house, for no retired colonel's pay, nor general's pay, for that matter, could have met the expenses of his large family, accustomed to every luxury; indeed, it was just enough to cover his own personal expenses, and provide a living for his widowed sister, who had been left penniless, but dared not earn her own living, since the custom of the country forbids women of class to do work of any kind.

His matronly wife with her six daughters (large families are the rule among these Latin Americans) had left the evening before, with several French maids, for Mar-de-la-Plata to spend the entire summer; he would be detained in the city for two weeks, and then—for freedom and the life he loved.

But he was strangely lonely; the house echoed his and the servants' footfalls with an intensity that made him nervous; the pillared corridors rang with no merry girlish laughter, and the luxuriantly furnished *patio* with its marble floors, and softly pattering fountains, seemed to mock him of his loneliness. Always before, he had left for the *estáncia* before his family had gone to Europe or the seashore for their summer outing, and he never would have believed that he—an old soldier—could be so overcome by sentiment.

He was minded to take up his abode for the next two weeks, previous to his leaving for the country, in his widowed sister's humble home, when the splendid thought came to him;—he would bring Francisco, his nephew, there with him to the lonely house.

For some time he had been drawn towards the little fellow, partly because his heart was desolate that he had no son of his own, partly because the boy was developing so many manly traits, and reminded him frequently, when he turned his round brown eyes towards him, of his own long since fallen soldier father.

He desired to know him better, to get closer to the lad—and now this was his opportunity; he would ask Anita to let him have Francisco for the summer, and the boy would keep the empty house lively for the few days until they should both leave for his Tres Arroyas ranch. He clapped his hands sharply, and a servant appeared.

"Have Enrique bring the motor car at four, when the afternoon is cooler," he ordered, and turned to his bed-room for the *siesta*, or rest, that all tropical and semitropical climates demand of their residents.

Week Twenty:
THE PLUMED SERPENT, QUETZALCOATL
Mexican Folk Tale
RETOLD BY FRONA EUNICE WAIT

Far as the eye could reach stretched the beautiful valley of Anahuac, where the air was sweet with the breath of flowers, and the earth seemed to melt perfectly into the sky.

"Oh! that mine eyes should see the splendor of this vision," said Mexi, the oldest of the wise men and the most learned, clasping his hands in rapture. "Oh! that I have been spared to see the fruition of thy will, great king and brother. Now may I go hence in peace."

As he ceased speaking he tottered and would have fallen had not one of the *tamanes* or porters, seated on mats under the shade of a giant oak, hastily risen, and caught him as his head fell forward on his bosom.

"The elements have undone thee," cried the Golden Hearted, kneeling hurriedly by his side and supporting the drooping head on his knee. "Thou art sadly in need of rest," he continued, alarmed at the pallor overspreading Mexi's finely wrinkled face.

The old man pushed the thin white locks of hair off his forehead, let the mantle slip back from his throat, and seemed to breathe easier.

"I am come to my final rest," he replied with a feeble smile. "It is not given me to enter the promised land."

The tawny, broad-shouldered, half-clad *tamanes*, laid down the thin cakes of ground corn they were eating and came near to the stricken old man, while the other wise men took off their hats and listened with bowed heads to what their comrade and leader said. They had stopped to rest and refresh themselves with food under the cool inviting shade of the trees where they could listen to the murmur of waterfalls, and feast, the eyes on the landscape surrounding them.

"There!" said Mexi, attracted by the buzzing of tiny wings, "is the green-throated humming-bird thou wert to follow as thy guide to the spot where a city is to be built in honor of the sun."

The Golden Hearted held up his hand with the forefinger extended and in a moment the little humming-bird lighted on it and looked at him curiously, as though obeying the will of some one. He did not touch it nor attempt to move for a few moments. Then he said:

"Little brother, spend the remainder of thy days with me. I need thee sorely, and have long waited for thy guidance."

In the meantime the wise men had given Mexi a cup of chocolate, not in a thin liquid like we know it, but thick like a cold custard, and with whipped goat's cream on top.

"Thou art kind," he said growing weaker and more faint all the time, "to try to prolong a life already spent." Turning his eyes toward the Golden Hearted he continued: "Lying next my heart thou wilt find a bundle of mystery. Carry it without opening until the time of thy departure from this strange land is at hand. Open then and thou wilt find directions for thy special work."

He did not speak again and when they tried to rouse him there was a smile of infinite peace on his face, but nothing save the lifeless body was before them. The gentle, sweet spirit of the old man had gone back to God.

"We will neither weep nor mourn for him," said the wise men to the Golden Hearted. "It would not be his wish, and we will show our love by obeying him."

And so they left him sleeping in a dell of ferns and mosses, in sight of Anahuac, the land by the side of water, as its name indicates, and continued their journey southward.

"The humming-bird alighted on his finger." Illustration by X. Martinez for Frona Eunice Wait in *The Stories of El Dorado* (San Francisco: Sunset Press, 1904).

On the way the wise men found a little creature, looking like a black currant with neither head, legs nor tail, so far as they could see. It is fat and dark and round, but if you squeeze him his blood is a brighter color than currant juice, and much more valuable because we get cochineal red of one, and currant jelly from the other. It was in the valley of Anahuac that the cochineal bug was first found, and it lives on the leaves of the prickly pear, or tuna cactus—the common kind with leaves shaped like a ham, and covered with long sharp needles.

The young cochineal bugs are so stupid that they must be tied on the leaves of the prickly pear to keep them from falling off and starving. In this way, too, they keep dry and warm in winter, but as soon as they are grown they are ruthlessly shaken to death and dried in the sun. Then the queer, shriveled dead bugs are put up in bags and sold.

"In the hot lands far to the south, the woods are full of rare orchids and other gems of the flower kingdom," said the Golden Hearted one day after a search for plants by the wayside, "but the vanilla bean is the only one fit for food. It will be well worth our while to study this strange branch of husbandry as soon as possible."

It was a long time before they came to a place near the seashore where a number of women were picking the ripe pods from vanilla vines which overran the trees and shrubs completely. The younger women had on bright-colored petticoats and gay scarfs over their long black hair, and they were storing the bean pods in wide-mouthed baskets strapped across their foreheads.

"What next do you do with these pods?" he asked of a young girl passing him with a full basket.

"We carefully assort them and then plunge the packages into hot water, before laying them out on mats to drain. For a week the beans are exposed to the heat of the sun, laid between woolen blankets. After this we pack them in *ollas* ["pots"] and keep them warm so as to promote fermentation while drying. This makes them soft, pliable, free from moisture, and of a dark chocolate color thickly frosted with needle-like crystals of acid."

And to this day if you buy vanilla beans they come in packages wrapped in silver foil, and have a delicious odor.

The bean is from six to nine inches long, and must be ground fine before it can be used in making the chocolate we are all so fond of, but it is dried and packed in the same manner as that described to the Golden Hearted.

It was not many days after leaving the wooded plains, that the travelers came in sight of four beautiful lakes with the frowning cliffs of Chapultepec outlined against the sky. Always on the alert for a sign the wise men said to each other in awe-stricken whispers:

"We must be near the place."

"Do you not see the rock with the flowering cactus!"

"And an eagle circling in the air with a serpent in its claws!"

"Oh! thou seen and unseen powers! search our hearts that thou mayst know all our gratitude," cried the Golden Hearted, falling on his knees and then prostrating himself on the ground, as did all the wise men.

"I am Guatamo," said a voice, and when the Golden Hearted looked up, a man old as Mexi stood blessing him. "Rise and receive word from thy father, the king from whom I am come. Fear me not; these hands have guided thy baby footsteps. Now must thou lend ear to my counsel."

The Golden Hearted was overjoyed to see some one from his father's court, and also glad to know that his wanderings in search of the place to honor the sun was over.

"This is not a promising outlook," said Guatamo, "but in the parchment scroll thou wilt find ample instructions to drain and render this a garden spot of exceeding loveliness. Hasten thy task since thy father is no longer living, and thy native land longs to see thee again."

Acting upon this advice the Golden Hearted and the wise men set to work at once to build the city, and to teach the willing natives to cultivate the land, and to make handsome mosaics out of the bright-colored feathers of the birds found in the forests in such numbers. Of course the birds were not killed to get their feathers, but in the royal gardens there were thousands of them kept during the moulting season, and then the feathers were picked up and assorted for use. Not only could they make perfect representations of birds and animals with them, but whole landscape scenes, including mountains, sea and sky. When finished it was necessary to touch them to know that feathers instead of paint had been used.

"'The Nahuas have come from Aztlan, the white country, and must be obeyed," was the word carried from one tribe to the other by the runners, and the wise men could only smile when they heard themselves called Nahuas, or wizards. The simple natives thought them capable of performing miracles because they were wise in the arts and knew how to heal the sick. The name of the Golden Hearted became Quetzalcoatl, the plumed serpent in their language, but we must remember that he wore the Quetzal plumes in his head-dress, the same as a king wears a gold and jeweled crown, and that a serpent in many of the languages of the ancient people meant a very wise man. In English we would say that the Golden Hearted was the wise king, which was not only true but a very simple name for him. The wonderful city he built was called Tenochtitlan, which signified "in honor of the sun," as his father had commanded him to do, and on the spot where it stood is the City of Mexico to-day. We shall hear very interesting things about the *teocalli*, or temple he built in Tenochtitlan, when we come to the story of "Montezuma and the Paba," for this is one of the most famous places in the new world, and no one can afford to be ignorant of its traditions and history.

Week Twenty:
MY NICARAGUA

When the Winter comes, I will take you to Nicaragua,
You will love it there!
You will love my home, my house in Nicaragua,
So large and queenly looking, with a haughty air
That seems to tell the mountains, the mountains of Nicaragua,
"You may roar and you may tremble, for all I care!"
      It is shadowy and cool;
      Has a garden in the middle where fruit-trees grow,
      And poppies, like a little army, row on row,
      And jasmine bushes that will make you think of snow,
      They are so white and light, so perfect and so frail,
      And when the wind is blowing they fly and flutter so!
The bath is in the garden, like a sort of pool,
With walls of honey-suckle and orchids all around.
The humming-bird is always making a sleepy sound.
      In the night there's the Aztec nightingale.
      But when the moon is up, in Nicaragua,
      The moon of Nicaragua and the million stars,
      It's the human heart that sings, and the heart of Nicaragua,
      To the pleading, plaintive music of guitars.

SALOMÓN DE LA SELVA
(1893–1959)

"Raven." Illustration for Francis Orpen Morris in *Bible Natural History* (Manchester: J. Ainsworth, 1856).

Week Twenty-One:

THE NAMING OF THE BIRDS

Alaskan Legend

RETOLD BY KATHARINE BERRY JUDSON

Now Raven went around among the birds, teaching them. He said to Grouse, "You are to live in a place where it is wintry. You will always live in a place high up so you will have plenty of breezes." Then Raven gave Grouse four white pebbles. He said, "You will never starve so long as you have these four pebbles."

Raven also said to Grouse, "You know that Sea-lion is your grandchild. You must get four more pebbles and give them to him." That is why the sea-lion has four large pebbles. It throws these at hunters. If one strikes a person, it kills him. From this story it is known that Grouse and Sea-lion understand each other.

Raven said to Ptarmigan, "You will be the maker of snowshoes. You will know how to travel in snow." It was from these birds that the Athapascans learned how to make snowshoes, and how to put the lacings on.

Raven came next to Wild Canary, that lives all the year around in the Tlingit country. He said, "You will be head among the very small birds. You are not to live on the same food as human beings. Keep away from them."

Then Raven said to Robin, "You will make people happy by your whistle. You will be a good whistler."

Then Raven said to Kun, the Flicker, "You will be chief among the birds of your size. You will not be found in all places. You will seldom be seen."

Raven said to Lugan, a bird that lives far out on the ocean, "You will seldom be seen near shore. You will live on lonely rocks, far out on the ocean."

When Raven came to Snipes, he said, "You will always go in flocks. You will never go out alone." Therefore we always see snipes in flocks.

Raven said to Asq-aca-tci, a small bird with yellow-green plumage, "You will always go in flocks. You will always be on the tree tops. That is where your food is."

Raven said to a very small bird, Kotlai, the size of a butterfly, "You will be liked. You will be seen only to give good luck. People will hear your voice, but seldom see you."

Then to Blue-jay Raven said, "You will have very fine clothes. You will be a good talker. People will take colors from your clothes."

Then Raven said to Xunkaha, "You will never be seen unless the north wind is going to blow." That is what the name Xunkaha means.

To Crow, Raven said, "You will make lots of noise. You will be great talkers." That is why, when you hear one crow, you hear a lot of others right afterward.

Raven said to Gusyiadul, "You will be seen only when warm weather is coming. Never come near except when warm weather is coming."

To Humming-bird Raven said, "People will enjoy seeing you. If a person sees you once, he will want to see you again."

Raven said to Eagle, "You will be very powerful and above all birds. Your eyesight will be very good. It will be easy for you to get what you want." Then Raven put talons on the eagle and said they would be useful to him.

Thus Raven taught all the birds.

Week Twenty-One:

THE FISHERMAN WHO CAUGHT THE SUN

Hawaiian Legend

RETOLD BY OLIVE BEAUPRÉ MILLER

Far across the blue Pacific Ocean, on the mountainous little island of Hawaii, a brown Hawaiian mother sat before a tiny straw-thatched hut, and told her little brown children stories. Before her the great round sun was sinking toward the ocean. Out on the water were big brown boys in their queer shaped canoes; others were swimming about, and some were riding the waves, standing up straight and balancing in a wonderful fashion on narrow boards that were carried landwards, rocking, and rolling, on the curling crests of the waves.

The younger children were all at home and grouped about their mother. They had decked themselves out gaily with garlands of flowers and long strings of colored seeds as they dearly loved to do, and, while they watched the setting sun, their mother told them, in the soft, musical Hawaiian tongue, an old Hawaiian tale:

"Many, many years ago, the Sun used to burst forth from the ocean at dawn and race so swiftly across the sky, that he would fling himself over the top of the great fire mountain and sink down again into the ocean before half a day's work was done. Sunset followed so quickly on sunrise that men began to complain:

"'Alas! The Sun, in his headlong haste, is cheating us of our due. We have not daylight enough to finish our hunting and fishing, to build our canoes, and gather our yams and bananas and cocoanuts. Night comes on and finds our work but half done.'

"Then there rose up a brave Fisherman and he said; 'I shall go to the Sun and teach him to make his journey as he should. He shall no more bolt across the sky at any pace he may choose.'

"The Fisherman's friends began to wail, and bid him remember what it meant to face such a powerful foe as the Sun. But the Fisherman never once stopped plaiting long ropes to make a snare, and he said; 'I do not fear the Sun. In this snare I shall catch him.'

So when the Sun had run his mad race for the day and left the world to night, the Fisherman got into his canoe and sailed out into the Eastern ocean. Far he sailed and farther through the shadows, down the silvery path that the moon lit up across the dark waste of the waters. Thus he came to the very edge of the earth, to the spot where the Sun would soon burst forth when he rose from under the ocean. And there he set his snare, gripping tight in his hands the ends of the rope from which he had made it.

"Soon the moon set and the world was wrapped in darkness. Then the Fisherman sat in his rocking canoe on the edge of the world and waited. At last the darkness faded into gray; bright jewels of light flashed now and again from the ocean. Purple and rose appeared in the sky and lo! a small rim of the sun peeped up to touch the white crests of the waves into fire and set all the ocean aflame.

"Still the Fisherman sat in his rocking canoe on the edge of the world and waited. In another moment a flood of gold streamed over the earth and the whole great Sun burst forth to begin his wild race across the sky. But ah! he had bolted straight into the snare and was tangled close in its meshes. Then the Fisherman rose in his canoe, and pulled tight the ropes in his hand. The great Sun raged! He flared and flamed, but the Fisherman held on fast.

"'Sun,' he cried, undaunted, 'from this day forth, you shall travel at proper speed. You shall no more do as you please and race at your own headlong pace across the sky. You shall give man a day that is long

Illustrated by Donn P. Crane for Olive Beaupré Miller in *Through Fairy Halls of My Bookhouse* (Chicago: The Bookhouse for Children, 1920).

enough so he may finish his hunting and fishing, build his canoes and gather his yams and bananas and cocoanuts.'

"The rage of the Sun grew scorching, withering, blasting. He struggled with all his might to be free. But the Fisherman braced his feet, balanced his rocking canoe on the waves, and held to the ropes with a grip that would never, never yield. At last the Sun saw he had met his master. Then he slowly softened his glare and stood still.

"I promise," he said, "I will race no more at my own headlong pace, but will travel at proper speed, slowly, steadily over the sky."

"When he had promised thus, the Fisherman set him free, but he did not remove from him all of the ropes. Some he left fastened securely at the edge of the world in order to bind him to keep his promise.

"You shall never again be free to have your own will," he said.

Then the Fisherman went back home and his people hailed him with music and singing, as one who had been their savior, for ever thereafter the Sun kept his word and the days were sufficiently long for all the work that had need to be done.

"But to this very day when the Sun rises or when he sets, you may still see the ropes hanging down. Look now, as he sinks toward the ocean! You say he is drawing water, but I tell you those brilliant rays that seem to anchor him to the sea, are in truth the meshes of that snare by which the Fisherman bound him."

Illustration from *Illustrated Index of British Shells* by G. B. Sowerby
(London: Simpkin, Marshall & Co., 1859).

Week Twenty-One:
SEA SHELL

Sea Shell, Sea Shell,
 Sing me a song, O Please!
A song of ships, and sailor men,
 And parrots, and tropical trees,

Of islands lost in the Spanish Main
 Which no man ever may find again,
Of fishes and corals under the waves,
 And seahorses stabled in great green caves.

Sea Shell, Sea Shell,
Sing of the things you know so well.
> AMY LOWELL
> (1874–1925)

Week Twenty-Two:

Charlotte's Quest

Canadian Short Story

by Lucy Maud Montgomery

Charlotte had made up her mind to see the Witch Penny about it. Perhaps God didn't think she ought to be unhappy, in a home of jolly, noisy, rollicking cousins (Charlotte hated noise and rollicking with all the power of her being); where she was continually being pounced on and petted and kissed (Charlotte detested pouncing and petting and kissing); where Aunt Florence or Cousin Edith or Mrs. Barrett, the grandmother of the gang, was always trying to dress her up like a doll (Charlotte hated to be dressed up); and where she was never alone or lonely for a moment (Charlotte loved and longed to be alone—well, not exactly lonely, because Charlotte was never lonely when she was alone). Yes, it was quite likely, Charlotte told herself, on considered reflection, that God couldn't believe that she was unhappy. So there remained only Witch Penny. Charlotte had an idea that witches were kittle cattle to have dealings with and that the thing was not altogether lawful. But she wanted a mother so desperately that she would have gone to any lengths to get one.

It was Jim who had told her about the Witch Penny very soon after she had come to live with Aunt Florence.

"The Witch Penny is going to fly to a witches' meeting tonight with her old black cat perched behind her," he told her one windy autumn evening. And then he went on with a fascinating rigmarole about riding on a broomstick over houses and hills. Jim did not mean to be fascinating. He was merely trying to frighten Charlotte "out of her skin." But Charlotte was not easily frightened and remained in her skin. She found his yarns thrilling, especially the part about flying on a broomstick, although she would have preferred to fly on a swallow's back. Why couldn't you, if you were a witch? If you could turn yourself into a grey cat, as Jim said Witch Penny could, why couldn't you turn yourself into something small enough to ride a swallow? Just think of swooping through the air. Charlotte quivered with ecstasy.

Charlotte wanted a mother terribly. She knew that the thing was quite possible.

Before father had gone away and just before she had come to Aunt Florence's, Nita Gresham had got a new mother. Charlotte heard about it in school. If Nita, why not she? A mother who would take you in her arms and tell you stories. To whom you would belong. It seemed a terrible thing to Charlotte that she didn't belong anywhere or to anybody. Not even to Father. How could you belong to a father who looked upon you merely as a hindrance to mountain climbing? Charlotte knew perfectly well that was how her father regarded her, although neither he nor anyone else had ever told her so. You couldn't fool Charlotte in all things. She might fall for a silly story about witches and broomsticks, but in some respects she had a terrible wisdom.

Next to a mother she wanted a quiet place where she could be alone when she wanted to be; to listen to the wind telling strange tales, or hold the big spotted shell that murmured of the sea to her ear, or talk to the roses in the garden. Or just sit still and think and say nothing. If you were quiet at Aunt Florence's, someone was sure to ask what was the matter with you. And if your visitation of silence was prolonged they said you were sulky. It had not been quite so bad when she had lived at home, a kind of home, with Father and old Mrs. Beckwith. At least they left her alone. If you couldn't be loved, the next best thing was to be let alone. At Aunt Florence's she was never let alone and she knew quite well they didn't love her. They kissed and petted and teased her just because it was one of their customs. Jim thought her a ninny.

Edith and Susette thought her a dumb-bell. Mrs. Barrett thought she was "queer," and Aunt Florence couldn't make her pretty.

"Goodness, child, are you all corners?" she would exclaim impatiently when Charlotte's dress wouldn't hang right. Aunt Florence hadn't any use for anyone with too many corners. And nothing else about Charlotte pleased her. She was too dark in a fair clan, her eyes were too big and grey, her eyebrows too bushy and her skin too sallow. "I don't know where she gets such a complexion," Aunt Florence mourned.

"Don't you? I do," said Mrs. Barrett very significantly. "She's the living image of You-Know-Who."

"I never saw her," said Aunt Florence, "but if Charlotte looks like her, I don't wonder Edward isn't fond of her."

So her father wasn't fond of her. Charlotte sighed. She had always suspected it, but it was a little bitter to be sure of it. She had always thought it was because he couldn't be fond of anything but mountain climbing. Now it seemed there was a mysterious You-Know-Who in the business.

Charlotte knew she didn't look like her mother. There was no picture of her mother that Charlotte had even seen, but she knew she had been small and fair and golden. Charlotte wished she looked like her mother. She couldn't remember her mother, that is, not exactly. She could only remember a dream she had had about her, a beautiful dream in which she was in such a beautiful place. And Mother was there with her. Charlotte had never forgotten it—she was always looking for it. An old house fronting seaward, ships going up and down. Spruce woods and misty hills, cold salt air from the water, rest, quiet, silence. And the most beautiful china lady, with blue shoes and a gilt sash and a red rose in her golden china hair, sitting on a shelf.

Mother had been there with her. Charlotte was quite sure of that, though everything else was a little dim, as dreams are. Charlotte always had a queer feeling that if she could find that place she would find Mother again. But it was not likely that even Witch Penny could help her to a place in a dream.

Charlotte determined to slip away on the afternoon they were getting ready for the party. They were always having parties. "Let us eat, drink and be merry," was the motto of the Laurences. Charlotte hated parties and she knew she would hate this more than most because they were going to have tableaux and Charlotte was to take part in one and wear a silly tinsel crown. Somehow, she hated the thought of that tinsel crown venomously.

In the customary scurry and bustle she hoped to get away unseen, but Mrs. Barrett spied her and asked her where she was going.

"I am going hunting for happiness," said Charlotte gravely and simply. The truth had to be told.

Mrs. Barrett stared at her.

"I don't know who you get your peculiar notions from. Any child but you would be keen to help get ready for a party. Look at your cousins—what a delightful time they're having."

Probably they were. Everybody was rushing wildly around, moving and dragging furniture about. But they were always doing that. Nothing ever remained in the same place longer than a week. Just as you got used to a thing being in a certain place, Aunt Florence or Susette took a notion it would look better somewhere else; and after much noisy, good-natured argument, there it went. And a party always gave such a grand excuse for moving everything.

Charlotte did not reply to Mrs. Barrett, which was another of her unsatisfactory habits. She simply opened the door, went out and shut it softly behind her. It was hard to shut it softly because, like every other door in the house, it seemed determined to bang shut. But Charlotte managed it.

She stood for a moment in the front porch, drawing a breath of relief. Behind her was noise and commotion. Edith and Susette were wrangling in the haft The radio was going full blare in the library, Jim was banging on the piano to make the fat dog howl—and the dog was howling. Charlotte put her fingers in her ears and ran down the walk. Over her was a grey, quiet autumn sky, and before her a grey, quiet road. Charlotte suddenly felt as light of being as if she really had been turned into a swallow. She was out, she was alone and she was going to find a mother.

The witch penny's house was a little grey one nestling against the steep hill that rose from the pond about half a mile west of the small town. The gate hung slackly on its hinges. The house itself was shabby and old, with sunken window sills and a much-patched roof. Charlotte reflected that being a witch didn't seem to be a very profitable business.

For a moment Charlotte hesitated. She was not a timid child, but she did feel a little frightened. Then she thought of Mrs. Barrett rocking fiercely in her rocker and forever talking in her high, cheerful voice. "Mother is always so bright," Aunt Florence always said. Charlotte shuddered. No witch could be worse. She knocked resolutely on the door.

A thumping sound inside ceased. Had she interrupted Witch Penny in the weaving of a spell? …and footsteps seemed to be coming down a stair. Then the door opened and Witch Penny appeared. Charlotte took her all in with one of her straight, deliberate looks.

She was grey as an owl, with a broad rosy face and tiny black eyes surrounded by cushions of fat. Charlotte thought she looked too jolly for a witch. But no doubt there were all kinds. Certainly the big black cat with fiery golden eyes that sat behind her on the lower step of the stair looked his reputed part.

"Now who may ye be and what may ye be wanting with me?" said Witch Penny a bit gruffly.

Charlotte never wasted breath, words or time. "I am Charlotte Laurence and I have come to ask you to find me a mother—that is, if you really are a witch. Are you?"

Witch Penny's look suddenly changed. It grew secretive and mysterious.

"Whist, child," she whispered. "Don't be talking of witches in the open daylight like this. Little ye know what might happen."

"But are you?" persisted Charlotte. If Witch Penny wasn't a witch, she wasn't going to bother with her.

"To be sure, I am. But come in, come in. Finding a mother ain't something to be done on the durestep. Better come right upstairs. I'm weaving a tablecloth for the fairies up there. All the witches in the countryside promised to do one apiece for them. The poor liddle shiftless craturs left all their tablecloths out in the frost last Tuesday night, and 'twas their ruination. But I've got far behind me comrades and mustn't be losing any more time. Ye'll excuse me if I kape on with me work while ye're telling me your troubles. It's the quane's own cloth I'm weaving, and it's looking sour enough her majesty will be if it's not finished on time."

Charlotte thought that Witch Penny's old loom looked very big and clumsy for the weaving of fairy tablecloths, and the web in it seemed strangely like rather coarse grey flannel, But no doubt witches had their own way of blinding the eyes of ordinary mortals. When Witch Penny finished it, she would weave a spell over it and it would become a thing of gossamer light and loveliness.

Witch Penny resumed her work and Charlotte sat down on a stool beside her. They were on a little landing above the stairs, with one low, cobwebby window and a stained ceiling with bunches of dried tansy and yarrow hanging from it. The cat had followed them up and sat on the top step, staring at Charlotte. Its eyes shone uncannily through the dusk of the staircase.

"Now, out with your story," said Witch Penny. 'Ye're wanting a mother, ye tell me, and ye're Charlotte Laurence. Ye'll be having Edward Laurence for your father, I'm thinking ?"

"Yes. But he's gone west to climb mountains," explained Charlotte. "He's always wanted to, but Mother died when I was three, and as long as I was small he couldn't. I'm eight now, so he's gone."

"And left ye with your Uncle Tom and your Aunt Florence. Oh, I've heard all about it. Your Aunt Florence's cat was after telling mine the whole story at the last dance we had. Your Aunt Florence do be too grand for the likes of us, but it's little she thinks where her cat do be going. Ye don't look like the Laurences—ye haven't got your father's laughing mouth—ye've got a proud mouth like your old Grandmother Jasper. Did ye ever see her?"

Charlotte shook her head. She knew nothing of her Grandmother Jasper beyond the fact of her existence, but all at once she knew who You-Know-Who was.

"No, it ain't likely ye would. She was real mad at your mother for marrying Ned Laurence. I've heard she never would forgive her, never would set foot in her house. But ye have her mouth. And what black hair ye've got. And what big eyes. And what little ears. And ye have a mole on your neck. 'Tis the witch's mark. Come now, child dear, wouldn't ye like to be made a witch? 'Tis a far easier job than the one ye've set me. Think av the fun av riding on the broomstick."

Charlotte thought of it. Flying over the steeples and dark spruces at night. "I think I'm too young to be a witch," she said.

Witch Penny's eyes twinkled.

"Sure, child dear, 'tis the young witches that do be having the most power. Mind ye, everybody can't be a witch. We're that exclusive ye'd never belave. But I'll not press ye. And ye want me to find you a mother?"

"If you please. Nita Gresham got a new mother. So why can't I?"

"Well, the real mothers are hard to come by. All the same, mebbe it can be managed. It's lucky ye've come in the right time of the moon. I couldn't have done a thing for ye next wake. And mind ye, child dear, I'm not after promising anything for sartin. But there's a chanct, there's a chanct …seeing as ye've got your grandmother's mouth. If ye'd looked like your father, it wouldn't be Witch Penny as'd help ye to a mother. I'd no use for him.

Witch Penny chuckled. "What kind of a mother do ye be wanting?"

"A quiet mother who doesn't laugh too much or ask too many questions."

Witch Penny shook her head.

"A rare kind. It'll take some conniving. Here…" Witch Penny dropped her shuttle, leaned forward and extracted from a box beside the loom a handful of raisins… "stow these away in your liddle inside while I do a bit av thinking."

Charlotte ate her raisins with a relish while Witch Penny wove slowly and thoughtfully. She did not speak until Charlotte had finished the last raisin.

"It come into me mind," said Witch Penny, "that if ye go up the long hill. . . and down it . . . then turn yourself about three times, nather more nor less, ye'll find a road that goes west. Folly your nose along it till ye come to a gate with a liddle lane that leads down to the harbour shore. Turn yourself about three times more… if ye forget that part of it, ye may look till your eyes fell out of your head, but niver a mother ye'll see. Then go down the lane to a stone house with a red door in it like a cat's tongue. Knock three times on the door. If there's a mother in the world for ye, ye'll find her there. That's all I can be doing for ye."

Charlotte got up briskly.

"Thank you very much. It sounds like a good long walk, so I ought to start. What am I to pay you for this?"

Witch Penny chuckled again. Something seemed to amuse her greatly.

"How much have ye got?" she asked.

"A dollar."

"How'd ye come by it?"

Charlotte thought witches were rather impertinent. However, if you dealt with them…

"Mrs. Beckwith gave it to me before she went away."

"And how come ye didn't spend it for swaties and ice cream?"

"I like to feel I've something to fall back on," said Charlotte gravely.

Witch Penny chuckled for the third time.

"Says your grandmother. Oh, ye're Laurence be name but it goes no daper. Kape your liddle bit av a dollar. Ye've got a mole on your neck. We can't charge folks as have moles anything. It's clane against our rules. Now run along or it'll be getting too late."

"I'm very much obliged to you," said Charlotte, putting her money back in her pocket and offering her thin brown hand.

"Ye do be a mannerly child at that," said Witch Penny.

Witch Penny stood on her sunken doorstep and watched the little, erect figure out of sight.

"Sure, and I do be wondering if I've done right. But she'd never fit in up at the Laurences with their clatter. And once the old leddy lays eyes on her!"

Charlotte had disappeared around the bend in the road. Then Witch Penny said a queer thing for a witch. She said: "God bless the liddle cratur."

CHARLOTTE TRAMPED STURDILY ON, adventurous and expectant. The sky grew greyer and the wind colder as she climbed the long hill. From the top she caught an unexpected, breath-taking view of a great grey harbour with white-capped racing waves. And beyond its sandy bar something greater and greyer still which she knew must be the sea. Charlotte stood for a few minutes in an ecstasy. She had never seen the harbour before, although she had known it was not far away. And yet, had she not? Charlotte felt bewildered. Her dream came back to her. She had seen this harbour in her dream, with the big waves racing to the shore and the black crows sitting on the fences of the fields and a white bird flying against the dark sky.

Charlotte went down the hill and gravely turned herself about three times. A wind that smelt of the sea came blowing down a road to the left. This must be what Witch Penny meant by following her nose. And sure enough, after Charlotte had walked along the road for a little while, there was the gate and a grassy, deep-rutted lane leading along the side of a gentle hill that sloped to the harbour.

Again Charlotte turned herself around. If there were no mother at the end of this quest, it should not be for any failure to perform Witch Penny's ritual scrupulously.

Halfway along the hill she came to the house, the grey stone house with the door like a cat's tongue, a house so grey and old that it seemed a part of the hill. It had a dignified, reposeful look as if it feared not what wind or rain could do to it.

Charlotte found her legs trembling under her. She had come to journey's end; and was there a mother in that house for her? Witch Penny hadn't seemed at all sure, she had only said there was a chance. It was beginning to rain, the harbour was dim and misty, it would soon be dark. Charlotte shivered, took her courage in both hands and knocked at the red door.

There was no answer. Charlotte waited awhile and then went around the house to the kitchen door—it was red, too—and knocked again.

The door opened. Charlotte felt a quick pang of disappointment. This was no mother: she was far too old for a mother, this tall, thin woman with a fine old face that might have been a man's and clear grey eyes with black bushy brows under frosty hair. Charlotte had never seen her before yet she had a queer feeling that the face was quite familiar to her.

"Who are you?" said the old woman, neither kindly nor unkindly … just in a simple, direct fashion to which Charlotte found it quite easy to respond.

"I am Charlotte Laurence. I went to Witch Penny to see if she could find me a mother and she told me to come here."

The old woman stood still for what seemed to Charlotte a very long moment. Then she stepped back and said, "Come in."

Charlotte looked around the little, white-washed kitchen. There was, to her further disappointment, no one in it, but she liked it. On the floor there was a big, dark-red, hooked rug, with three black cats in it. The cats had yellow wool eyes that were quite bright and catty in spite of the fact that they had evidently been walked over a good many years. There was a great stove with front doors that slid so far back that it was as good as a fireplace. There was a low wide window looking out on the harbour. There was a table with a red-and-white checkered cloth on it and a platterful of something that smelt very good to Charlotte after her long walk.

"I was just sitting down to supper," said the old woman. "I had a feeling that I was going to have company so I cooked a bit extra. Take off your cap and coat and sit in."

Charlotte silently did as she was told. The old woman sat down, said grace…Charlotte liked that…and gave Charlotte a plentiful helping of crisp bacon and pancakes with maple syrup poured over them. Charlotte devoted herself to the business of eating. She had never been so hungry in her life before and she had never eaten anything that tasted so good as the bacon and pancakes. It was now raining and blowing quite wildly but the stove was glowing clear red in the dusk and the peace and cosiness of the old kitchen was in delightful contrast to the storm outside. And just to eat supper in silence, not having to talk or laugh unless you really wanted to, was so heavenly. Charlotte thought of the noisy meals at Aunt Florence's where everybody talked and laughed incessantly… Aunt Florence liked "cheerful meals."

OF COURSE, AS YET THERE WAS NO MOTHER. But one must have patience. It was easy to be patient here. Charlotte found herself liking the house… feeling at home in it. It was not strange to her… and the old woman was not strange. Charlotte wondered where she had seen eyes like that before, many times before. And she loved the house. She wanted to see the hidden things in it—not its furniture or its carpets, but the letters in old boxes upstairs, and faded photos and clothes in old trunks. It seemed as if they belonged to her. She sighed in pure happiness. The old woman did not ask her why she sighed. That, too, was heavenly.

When the meal was over, the old woman—after all Charlotte was beginning to think she wasn't so very old, it was just her white hair made you think so—put Charlotte in a chair by the stove where she could toast her feet on the warm hearth, and washed the dishes. Her shadow darted in all directions over the kitchen walls and ceiling and sometimes looked more like a witch than Witch Penny. But this woman was not a witch. Somehow, Charlotte felt no qualms on that score.

When the old woman had put her dishes away in a little corner cupboard with glass doors and shelves trimmed with white, scalloped lace paper, she lighted a lamp, got out her knitting and sat down by the table.

"You're Charlotte Laurence. And your father, I suppose, was Edward Laurence."

Charlotte nodded.

"Where is he?"

"He has gone to climb mountains in British Columbia and he sent me to stay with Aunt Florence while he was away."

"How long is he going to be away?"

"Years," said Charlotte indifferently.

The old woman knitted two rounds of her stocking before she said anything else.

"Do you like it at your Aunt Florence's?"

"No. It's too noisy and affectionate," said Charlotte gravely.

The old woman laid down her knitting and stared at her. There was a queer expression on her face, she might almost have been going to laugh. Her thick black eyebrows twitched.

"Does your aunt know where you are?"

Charlotte shook her head.

"And don't you think she'll be worried? I don't think you can get back tonight in this storm."

"She's always worried over something," said Charlotte, as if it didn't matter a great deal. Nobody had ever worried much about her. And she was very well satisfied with where she was. She had never been in a place or in such company that suited her so well. Only, as yet, no mother. But it was quiet and peaceful and warm. The wood snapped and crackled in the stove. The rain spattered on the window panes. The wind growled and snarled because it could not get into the sturdy house.

"We're neither of us much for talking, it seems," said the old woman.

"No, but I think we are entertaining each other very well," said Charlotte.

This time the old woman did really laugh.

"I've had some such thought myself," she said.

It was quite a long while, a long, delightful while, after that Charlotte found herself nodding. And the downtrodden black cats had begun to trot around the rug.

"You're half asleep. You'd be better in bed. Are you afraid to sleep alone?"

Afraid? Charlotte loved to sleep alone. And she never could at Aunt Florence's. She did not even have a steady room, always being passed about from one to the other. Now Mrs. Barrett who snored, now Jenny who kicked, now Edith or Susette who fussed over her.

"I like sleeping alone," said Charlotte.

The old woman filled a little blue rubber bag with hot water from the puffing kettle and lighted a candle in a little blue china candlestick. She took Charlotte through a large room, with only a little plain furniture in it. You could move around in it without knocking something over. It was not cluttered up with over-stuffed divans or gilt fandangos, but full of dancing, inviting shadows from the candle. Charlotte felt sure that this room was never in a hurry. Then they went up a staircase of shining black steps and into a bedroom where there was a bed with a pink flounced spread. The old woman set the candle on the bureau, turned back the bedclothes and put the blue bottle in the bed.

"I hope you'll be warm and have a good night," she said. There was something in her face that was very kind. Charlotte felt emboldened to ask a question.

"Would you mind telling me if I'm likely to find a mother here?"

"We'll see about that in the morning," said the old woman as she went out and shut the brown door with the big brass latch.

Charlotte looked about the room. She loved it: and it was a room that was used to being loved. Charlotte was quite sure of that. It had a hooked rug on the floor with great soft plushy roses and ferns in it, flowered chintz curtains at the window, and a blue-and-white pitcher and wash basin. And everything in it felt related to her.

On the wall over the table was the picture of a little girl in an old-fashioned dress… a little girl not much older than Charlotte. She looked very sweet and young and innocent with the little puffs at her shoulders and the big bow of ribbon in her hair. Charlotte felt acquainted with her.

And then she saw it, the china lady with the blue shoes and the gilt sash and the unfaded red rose in her golden hair, sitting on the little frilled shelf in the comer… the china lady of her dream. There could be no mistake about it. Sometime she had been here before… not in a dream but really. And her mother had been with her.

Charlotte got into bed, feeling perfectly at home. When she wakened in the morning to see sunshine raining all over her bed, the old woman was bending over her.

"Is that Mother's picture?" were the first words Charlotte said.

"Yes. This used to be her room. This is not the first time you have been in it. Have you any recollection of it, child?"

"Yes. I thought it was a dream until last night. And Mother was here with me, wasn't she?"

"Yes. I am your grandmother, Elizabeth Jasper. Your mother married a man I'd no use for. People will tell you I never forgave her. That was nonsense. It's true I never went to see her. I wouldn't cross the threshold of Ned Laurence's house. But she came here to see me and brought you. We made up for all our coolness. She died soon afterwards. I couldn't bring myself to have anything to do with your father. I see I was wrong. I shouldn't have left him to bring you up to hate me."

"But he didn't. He just never said anything about you," said Charlotte, sitting up in bed. She knew now that no new mother was to be found, but somehow she did not feel disappointed. She seemed so close to her own mother. The room, the house, was full of her.

"Judith Penny sent you here to find a mother. She isn't called a witch for nothing, that one. I'm sorry I haven't got a mother for you. Do you think a grandmother would do?"

Charlotte knew all at once where she had seen Grandmother Jasper's eyes so often. In her looking glass. She was suddenly so happy that it seemed to her she must burst with her happiness.

"Can I live here with you?" she whispered. Grandmother Jasper nodded.

"I telephoned your aunt last night after you went to bed and told her where you were. I told her you might stay here quite likely. She didn't seem to mind."

"Oh, she wouldn't. Grandmother, it's so quiet here!"

Grandmother nodded.

"We're alike in more than our looks, child. What a turn you gave me when I opened the door last night. I thought I was seeing the ghost of the child I was fifty years ago."

"Grandmother," said Charlotte curiously, "is Witch Penny really a witch?"

"If she isn't, she ought to be," said Grandmother Jasper.

Week Twenty-Two:
THE MONEY-CHEST
Icelandic Legend
RETOLD BY JÓN ARNASON

It happened, once upon a time, that a large party of men were travelling together, and pitched their tent, early one Sunday morning, on the fresh sward of a fair green meadow. The weather was bright and warm, and the men being tired with their night's journey, and having tethered their horses, fell asleep, side by side, all round the inside of the tent. One of them, however, who happened to be lying nearest the door, could not, in spite of his fatigue, succeed in getting to sleep, so lay idly watching the other sleepers. As he looked round he discovered a small cloud of pale-blue vapour moving over the head of the man who was sleeping in the innermost part of the tent. Astonished at this he sat up, and at the same moment the cloud flitted out of the tent. Being curious to know what it could be and what would become of it, he jumped up softly, and, without awaking the others, stole out into the sunshine. On looking round he saw the vapour floating slowly over the meadow, so set himself to follow it. After a while it stopped over where lay the blanched skull of a horse upon the grass, in and about which hummed and buzzed a cloud of noisy blue flies. Into this the vapour entered among the flies. After staying a while, it came out, and took its course over the meadow till it came to a little thread of a rivulet, which hurried through the grass. Here it seemed to be at a loss how to get over the water, and moved restlessly and impatiently up and down the side of it, till the man laid his whip, which he happened to have with him, over it, the handle alone being sufficient to bridge it across. Over this the vapour passed and moved on till it came to a small hillock, into which it disappeared. The man stood by and waited for it to come out again, which it soon did, and returned by the same way as that by which it had come. The man laid his whip as before across the stream and the vapour crossed upon the handle. Then it moved on towards the tent, which it entered, and the man who had followed it saw it hover for a minute over the head of the sleeper, where he had first seen it, and disappear. After this he lay down again, and went to sleep himself.

When the day was far spent and the sun was going down, the men rose, struck the tent, and made preparations for beginning their journey again. While they were packing, and loading the horses, they talked on various things, and, among others, on money.

"Bless me!" said the man who had slept in the innermost part of the tent, "I wish I had what I saw in my dream to-day."

"What was your dream, and what did you see?" asked the man who had followed the vapour.

The other replied, "I dreamt that I walked out from the tent, and across the meadow till I came to a large and beautiful building, into which I went. There I found many people at revel in a vast and noble hall, singing, dancing, and making merry. I stayed some time among them, and when I left them and stepped out from the hall, I saw stretched before me a vast plain of fair green sward. Over this I walked for some time, till I came to an immensely broad and turbulent river, over which I wished to cross, but could find no means of doing so. As I was walking up and down the bank thinking how I could possibly get over it, I saw a mighty giant greater than any I had ever heard of, come towards me, holding in his hand the trunk of a large tree, which he laid across the river. Thus I was able to get easily to the other side. The river once passed, I walked straight on for a long time till I came to a high mound which lay open. I went into it, thinking to find wonderful treasures, but found only a single chest, which, however, was so full of money that I could neither lift it, nor, though I spent hours over it, count the quarter of its contents. So I gave it up and bent my steps hither again. The giant flung his tree across the river as before, and I came to the tent and went to sleep from sheer weariness."

At hearing this, the other who had followed the vapour was mightily pleased, and, laughing to himself, said, "Come, my good fellow, let us fetch the money. If one could not count it, no doubt two can."

"Fetch the money!" replied the man. "Are you mad ? Do you forget that I only *dreamed* about it? Where would you fetch it from?"

But as the other seemed really earnest and determined, he consented to go with him.

So they took the same course as the vapour had taken, and when they came to the skull, "There is your hall of revel," said the man who had followed the mist some hours before.

"And there," he said, when they stepped over the rivulet, "is your broad and turbulent river, and here the trunk the giant threw over it as a bridge." With these words he showed him his whip.

The other was filled with amazement, and when they came to the mound, and having dug a little way into it, really and truly discovered a heavy chest fall of golden pieces, his astonishment was not a whit the less. On their way back to the tent with the treasure, his companion told him all about the matter.

Whether they complained of the weight of the money-chest or gave up counting its contents in despair, this history relateth not.

Four Times of the Day: Night (detail, 1757) by French artist Claude-Joseph Vernet. Art Gallery of South Australia, Adelaide.

Week Twenty-Two:
THE NIGHT COMETH

Work! for the night is coming;
    Work! through the morning hours;
Work! while the dew is sparkling;
    Work! 'mid the springing flowers;
Work! while the day grows brighter,
    Under the glowing sun;
Work! for the night is coming, —
    Night, when man's work is done.

Work! for the night is coming;
    Work! through the sunny noon;
Fill the bright hours with labour,
    Rest cometh sure and soon.
Give to each flying minute
    Something to keep in store;
Work! for the night is coming, —
    Night, when man works no more.

Work! for the night is coming;
    Under the sunset skies,
While their bright tints are glowing,
    Work! for the daylight flies;
Work! till the last beam fadeth,
    Fadeth to shine no more;
Work! while the night is darkening,—
    Night, when man's work is o'er.

ANNIE LOUISA WALKER
(1836–1907)

Week Twenty-Three:
TERETÉ, THE BOY IN THE MOON
New Zealand Folk Tale
RETOLD BY KATE MCCOSH CLARK

"I want the moon! I want the moon!" Such was the frequent cry of a little boy named Tereté, who lived on an island where coco-nut trees fringed the shining beach, on which the gentle waves curled with a pleasant murmur. And bright flowers bloomed on that isle, and birds with glittering plumage filled the woods, and many-coloured fishes played in the clear water inside the coral reef. Yet little Tereté was discontented, and was constantly crying for something or other. His sister was a kind-hearted girl, and in order to please him she often gave him dainties, the steamed kernels of fruits, or the warmed milk of the coco-nut. Still Tereté was nearly always grumbling, in fact, the only time when he seemed really happy was when he could see the moon shining in the sky. Then he loved to be out in the soft summer nights, and he dried his eyes and sung merrily.

One day when Tereté's father came back from fishing, he found the boy moping by himself under a tree, looking more miserable than usual, and he said to him, "What a silly boy you are Tereté, not to be happy as the day is long. See how the sun shines and the flowers open their bright blossoms. There are plenty of good fruits round you, and you have nothing to do but sit in the sun, play on the sands, or fish off the rocks all day. What more do you want?"

"I want the moon, father. Oh, the moon! The moon!" And Tereté's voice rose higher and higher as he wept bitterly. His father looked at him wonderingly, and then said:

"Well, my boy, I cannot get you the moon, nor can I make it always shine. But if you will come with me to-night in my canoe I will take you to the moon. Then, perhaps, you will be happy."

"O thank you, father, thank you," said Tereté joyfully, and he dried his tears and amused himself all day decorating the canoe with white shells and flowering creepers, making it look pretty for the voyage to the moon.

His brothers were astonished to see him so happily employed, and said to each other, "Where are Tereté's tears to-day? How is it that he is not crying his heart out for the moon?"

But Tereté's sister was sad and said nothing, for she knew why. At last the evening came, and the sun's last rays flashed across the level sea. Then quickly all was dark. Before beginning supper Tereté's father poured out a libation to the gods. Then he blew up the little fire of coco-nut leaves, and said:

"This fire is for you, O ye gods. Let no evil thing befall us."

Thus prayed he in order to propitiate the gods for his boy's voyage to the moon.

Then the father and children sat down cross-legged, as was the custom, to their evening meal. When it was finished Tereté's father said, "Now, my child, we must go, for darkness covers the land and sea." When Tereté looked out into the night he could not help crying a little, but his father smiled and said, "The moon will soon be up, and will dry your tears, my boy. Come let us start, for we must get to the edge of the ocean by the time the moon rises, so that I can give you to him."

His sister gave Tereté a last drink of warm coco-nut milk, and then, sad at heart, took her little brother's hand, and they all went down to the shore together. Tereté's spirits soon rose, for the stars were flashing out one by one, and luminous points of light gleamed everywhere on the wet sand and in the breaking water, as though the lights of myriad tiny fire-flies were entangled in the waves. And the flowers that decorated the canoe gave out sweet scents as some of Teretés playfellows and his brothers crushed them in their hands when they pulled the canoe down to the water. Then, as Tereté and his father left the shore, bright careless voices called out: "Good-bye, Tereté, good-bye! Come back soon and tell us what the moon is like."

But his sister said nothing. She knew he would never come back, and, her dark eyes full of tears, she watched the canoe till it was but a blot on the waters. She saw the moon rise, then she went back to her bed of leaves in the little hut, but sleep that night was far from her.

Little Tereté sat silent in the canoe. His father had put up the coco-nut-mat sail to catch the rising breeze, and they were speeding over the waters. Soon the island shore was lost in the distance. After a while the father said:

"I suppose you still wish to go to the moon, my son?" for he had noticed how quiet the boy was.

Tereté did not reply; only the gurgle of the waters was heard against the prow of the canoe as they sailed on.

"We can still go back if you wish," continued his father; "but if I give you to the moon you will never come back. Will you not be happy with us on our island home? You are dear unto us, O my son."

But Tereté answered not; he had heard what his father said, but his heart was full. He almost wished to go back, but he did not like to say so. The moonland was a long way off, and perhaps the moon would not look so nice when he got there as it did from the earth. But if he returned his companions would laugh at him, and there would be the heat and the glare of the sun, and then, what untold delights might be in the soft light of the unknown moonland. So thought Tereté. And all the time they were sailing on and on to the edge of the sea.

When the bright rim of the full moon rose above the gently moving waves, and the soft rays began to spread out into a stretch of dancing light, Tereté cried joyfully:

"The moon! the moon!" and he forgot all about his home and his sister and brothers as he stretched out his arms to the fast rising moon.

"Come!" said his father, "come!" and he lifted Tereté in his arms and placed him on the moon; and he said, "Good-bye, my boy, good-bye."

But Tereté scarcely heard his words, so wrapt was he in delight of the moon's beauty; and the boy's face shone with an unearthly brightness as he was borne aloft. Once only as his eyes rested for a second on the departing canoe did he sigh dreamily, "Good-bye, father."

Away sailed the moon with the boy far into the heights of the summer sky. Away sailed his father's boat, looking like a dark sea-bird on the waters below.

Little Tereté never came back to his island home, though on bright moonlight nights his sister would go down to the shore and, stretching out her hands, prayed: "O moon, give him back to me; give back my little brother!" But no answering voice came from the moon or child to cheer her heart.

The islanders say that on clear nights they can still see the boy sitting in the moon; for there death enters not; all stays for ever bright and fair.

The people now call Tereté "the child of the moon," and when the new moon comes they salute it and say:

"O child of the moon! we rejoice that you have come." And before going on any war expedition the warriors may be heard chanting these words:

> *O child of the moon,*
> *Our pathway make clear,*
> *In hours of dark danger*
> *Let thy light be near.*
> *Fill the hollows with brightness*
> *Till night is as day.*
> *And with sure-footed lightness*
> *We speed on our way.*

Whether little Tereté is happy we cannot tell.

Week Twenty-Three:

THE GRAVE

Jamaican Folk Tale

BY STANLEY JONES

Once Mrs. Anansi had a large feed. She planted it with peas. Anansi was so lazy he would never do any work. He was afraid that they would give him none of the peas, so he pretended to be sick. After about nine days, he called his wife an' children an' bid them farewell, tell them that he was about to die, an' he ask them this last request, that they bury him in the mids' of the peas-walk, but firs' they mus' make a hole thru the head of the coffin an' also in the grave so that he could watch the peas for them while he was lying there. An' one thing more, he said, he would like them to put a pot and a little water there at the head of the grave to scare the thieves away. So he died and was buried.

All this time he was only pretending to be dead, an' every night at twelve o'clock he creep out of the grave, pick a bundle of peas, boil it, and after having a good meal, go back in the grave to rest. Mistress Anansi was surprised to see all her peas being stolen. She could catch the thief no-how. One day her eldest son said to her, "Mother, I bet you it's my father stealing those peas!" At that Mrs. Anansi got into a temper, said, "How could you expect your dead father to rob the peas!" Said, "Well, mother, I soon prove it to you." He got some tar an' he painted a stump at the head of the grave an' he put a hat on it.

When Anansi came out to have his feast as usual, he saw this thing standing in the groun'. He said, "Good-evening, sir!" got no reply. Again he said, "Good-evening, sir!" an' still no reply. "If you don' speak to me I'll kick you!" He raise his foot an' kick the stump an' the tar held it there like glue. "Let me go, let me go, sir, or I'll knock you down with my right hand!" That hand stuck fast all the same. "If you don' let me go, I'll hit you with my lef' hand!" That hand stick fas' all the same. An' he raise his lef' foot an' gave the stump a terrible blow. That foot stuck. Anansi was suspended in air an' had to remain there till morning. Anansi was so ashamed that he climb up beneath the rafters an' there he is to this day.

Week Twenty-Three:
THE KIND MOON

I think the moon is very kind
   To take such trouble just for me.
He came along with me from home
   To keep me company.

He went as fast as I could run;
   I wonder how he crossed the sky?
I'm sure he has n't legs and feet
   Or any wings to fly.

Yet here he is above their roof;
   Perhaps he thinks it is n't right
For me to go so far alone,
   Tho' mother said I might.

SARA TEASDALE
(1 8 8 4 – 1 9 3 3)

"Speeding away across the country as swift as the wind." Illustration by A. J. Johnson for Atha Westbury in *Australian Fairy Tales* (London: Ward, Lock & Company, 1897).

Week Twenty-Four:
KING DUNCE
Australian Folk Tale

BY ATHA WESTBURY

Only a careless, stupid boy perched on a high stool within the schoolroom, trying to learn his lesson, long after his companions had been dismissed to their several homes. Only the biggest dunce at Slate-em's Academy, who wouldn't try, like other boys, to master his tasks— not because he hadn't the ability to do so, but because he wanted to be a King. Yes, dear readers, Noel Biffin, son of Jack Biffin, the tin-smith, wanted to be a King. Nothing less would satisfy him. No, not even the rank of Duke or Prince; so, instead of minding his lessons, young Biffin drew Kings on his slate and in his copy-book, and was therefore compelled to ride the wooden horse after school hours.

It was a very beautiful evening, with a grand sunset glow flooding Slate-em's Academy, and wrapping the Dunce round and round as with an amber-coloured mantle, orange tinted. The old usher, nodding in his chair, was quite unconscious of the halo which played round and about his bald, venerable head, and made him appear for one brief moment like one of the Apostles. The good, patient old man was tired with the heat, and weary with the incessant chatter of the boys, and so he dozed in comfort, and saw not the wee, shapely creature who entered at the window and approached the boy as he stood upon the stool and bent the knee before him. Although small, the stranger was very handsome, and decked from head to heel in bright, glittering armour, with a crimson plume adorning his helmet.

"May it please your gracious Majesty," he said, doffing his helmet, "my name is Popgun—Sir Guy Fawkes Popgun, Knight—one of your Majesty's subjects from the realm of Shadowland." The Dunce nearly fell from the stool in amazement at the strange words. He looked towards the still sleeping master, and from him to the armour-clad Knight at his feet, and replied in a low tone, "Hush! Don't speak so loud. I haven't learnt my lesson yet; if he wakens he'll thrash me. Now, what do you want?"

"Pardon, your liege," rejoined the Knight respectfully, "I am sent as ambassador from the good people of Shadowland to inform your Majesty that you have been unanimously elected monarch of our wide and spacious dominions, and I beg that it may please you to allow me to conduct you thither without delay."

"A King! Am I really a King after all?" cried Biffin, jumping from the stool.

"Every inch a King, your Majesty," replied Sir Guy Fawkes Popgun, replacing his headpiece. "Will your liege follow me?"

"Stop, where is Shadowland?" inquired the boy.

"On the borders of Fancy, where dwell my kindred, the Australian elves. Fairyland will have none but a mortal to reign over her. Come, your Majesty." And with a dignified bearing the Elfin Knight strode past the slumbering usher, and led the newly-elected Majesty of Elfland out at the door, which opened at their approach. Beyond the school, out on the open play-ground, stood two fine-looking emus, splendidly caparisoned, and ready for a journey; and before young Biffin knew what he was about he and his companion were mounted thereon, and were speeding away across the country as swift as the wind. Small townships, hills and valleys, tracts of gloomy forests, and broad lakes appeared before them, and disappeared behind them again, before the boy could say "Jack Robinson."

Indeed, poor Biffin hadn't breath to say anything, they proceeded so swiftly. At length they came to a large sandy desert on the confines of which rose a chain of lofty mountains. After crossing the desert these mountains looked so steep and high that further progress appeared at an end, but the Knight went to a cave close by and brought forth a pair of flying horses, which flew upward with them in a moment and landed them far away on the other side in safety—and this was Shadowland of the Elfins. What poet's brain, teeming with strange wild fancies, could give expression to such a scene of loveliness as Noel the Dunce saw here? What travel-stained worshipper of Nature, traversing the girdle of the globe, ever feasted his eyes on a more glorious prospect? Not at Rome, filled as it is with monuments of man; nor at Athens, where Paul found the tablet inscribed, "To the Unknown God"; or on that Ionian Isle, where the inspired John wrote "The Revelation." Beautiful and sacred are all three to view, but I have feasted my soul on scenes equally grand and sublime in this new land where the Universal Spirit of "Our Father" seemed to rest, and attract the uplifted eyes and the inmost thoughts of the Soul to the Invisible Presence.

The flying steeds alighted in a ravine shut in by walls of fantastic rocks, peaked and turreted like the gable of some old feudal castle. Here a mounted escort, composed of the potent and mighty of the empire, awaited their coming, and led the King upwards to a grassy platform, shaded by a patch of hoary trees, where a throne built of wild-flowers had been erected for his reception. The site commanded a fine view of the surrounding country, and the elected monarch beheld with satisfaction thousands and thousands of his subjects assembled on the plains below to do him homage, and whose cheers and shouts rang far and wide when he ascended the throne to read the proclamation.

From time to time, for generations past, the Elfin Kings had to read their own proclamations, but when young Biffin received the paper from the hands of the Prime Minister his heart sank within him. His progress at school had been so slow that he was unable to read print fluently. How, then, was he to master the contents of the closely-written parchment in his hand? At that moment he would have given all his toys at home, even to his crop-eared pony, to have been able to read writing; but he couldn't read or spell, nor make anything better than a pot-hook.

"May it please your Majesty to read the proclamation to the people?" whispered Sir Guy Fawkes Popgun in the King's ear.

"I—I cannot read," replied his Majesty, trembling with shame and vexation.

"*Cannot read!*" repeated the courtiers, looking at each other. "Surely your Majesty is jesting."

"Indeed, gentlemen, I'm afraid I'm a dunce," replied Biffin sheepishly.

"A dunce, who cannot read, and yet has the silly presumption to be a King!" shouted the fairy populace in a mocking tone. "Hurrah for King Dunce! Long live King Dunce!"

And such is the uncertainty of popular favour in Elfland, that the vast assembly, who but a moment before had exhibited such hearty tokens of good-will, began to hoot and clamour in derision. They pulled the monarch from his throne, stripped him of his robes of state, and carried him to a rocky peak, where they doffed his crown and replaced it with a wreath of straw; while their shouts "Long live King Dunce! Hurrah for King Dunce!" once more rent the air.

In all his troubles at home, and his canings and disappointments with his lessons at school, our hero never felt so humbled and crest-fallen in his life before. He would have given anything to be enabled to read and write well. And this wish would have been easily gratified, had he but paid a little attention to his books while at the Academy; but he hadn't done so, and the result was his downfall from the proud position he had so long coveted.

What availed his regrets *now*, when he was led away a prisoner, and placed in a dark cave, guarded by seven monsters, whose bodies were covered with long feathers, and who had heads like monkeys? It availed nothing that they set him hard lessons day and night, beat him with rods, until he was bruised all over, and suffered such pain that he made his escape from the cave. But the monsters were after him across the country, over hill and dale, until he came to the top of the high mountain which overlooked the desert, and the monsters being close behind, there was nothing left for him in his last extremity but to leap for his life and liberty.

And Noel Biffin did leap; but instead of being dashed to pieces, the Dunce came down from his perch on the stool to the floor of the schoolroom, the noise of which roused the usher from his nap, who gave the stupid boy a dose of cane pie and sent him home.

"Pelican." Illustration by unknown illustrator for Francis Orpen Morris in *Bible Natural History* (Manchester: J. Ainsworth, 1856).

Week Twenty-Four:

GOOLAYYAHLEE THE PELICAN

Australian Folk Tale

RETOLD BY KATIE LANGLOH PARKER

At one time the Daens had no fishing nets, nor then had they the stone fisheries which Byamee afterwards made for them, the best model of which is still to be seen at Brewarrina.

In order to catch fish in those days they used to make a wall of poligonum and grass mixed together, across the creek; then go above it and drive the fish down to it, catching them with their hands against the break or wall. Or they would put these breaks across a mubboon or small tributary of the main creek, as a flood was going down, and, as the water ran out of the mubboon, fish would be caught in numbers in the break.

Goolayyahlee the pelican, a great wirreenun, was the first seen with a net. But where he had obtained it from, or where he kept it, no one knew for a long while. When he wanted to fish he used to tell his children to go and get sticks for the ends of the net, that they might go fishing.

"But where is the net?"

"It will be here when you come back. You do what I tell you. Get the sticks."

Frightened to ask more the children went to break the sticks which Goolayyahlee said must be of Eurah, a drooping shrub growing on the banks of the creeks, or near swamp oak-scrub. This shrub bore masses of large cream bell-shaped flowers, spotted with brown, beautiful to look at, but sickening to smell: where no dheal grew this shrub was used in place of that sacred tree.

When the children brought back the eurah sticks, there on the ground in front of their father was the big fishing net, ten or twelve feet long, and four or five feet wide. Beside it was a small smoke fire of budta twigs, on to which Goolayyahlee now threw some of the eurah leaves, and when the smoke was thick he held the net in it. Then, taking the net with them, down they all went into the water, where two men with the net—through the ends of which were the eurah sticks—went down stream to a shallow place, where they stationed themselves one at each end of the net stretched across the creek between them. The others went up stream and splashed about to frighten the fish down to the net, in which some were soon caught.

When they had enough they would come out, make fires and cook the fish. Every fishing-time the tribe puzzled over the question as to how and where Goolayyahlee had obtained this valuable net, and as to where he kept it, for after each fishing-time he took it away and no one saw it again until they went fishing; his wife and children said he never took it to his humpie.

One day the children thought that when they were sent for the eurah sticks, some of them would hide and watch where their father did get this net from. They saw him, when he thought they were safely out of sight, begin to twist his neck about and wriggle as if in great pain. They thought he must be very ill and were just coming from their hiding place, when all of a sudden he gave a violent wriggle, contorting himself until his neck seemed to stretch to an immense length; the children were too frightened at his appearance to move; they stayed where they were, speechless, huddled together, their eyes fixed on their father, who gave another convulsive movement and then, to their amazement, out through his mouth he brought forth the fishing net.

So that was where he kept it, inside himself. The children watched him drawing it out, until it all lay in a heap in front of him, then down he sat beside it, apparently none the worse, to await their return.

The children who had been hiding ran to meet the others, whom they told what they had seen. They were so excited at their discovery that they talked much about it, and soon the secret hiding-place of the net was a secret no longer, but as yet no one knew how it was made. At last Goolayyahlee grew tired of having to produce his net so often, for the fame of this new method of fishing had spread throughout the country; even strange tribes came to see the wonderful net. He told the people to do as he had done, and make nets for themselves. Then he told them how to do it. They were to strip off mooroomin, or Noongah bark, take off the hard outside part, then chew the softer part, and work it into twine, with which they could make the nets though he only, he said, swallowed the fibre, and it worked itself up into a net inside him; but that was because he was a great wirreenun; others could not do so.

After that all the tribes made fishing-nets, but only the tribe of Goolayyahlee could work the fibre inside them into nets, which the pelicans do to this day, the Daens say. And the Daens tell you that if you watch the Goolayyahlee or pelicans fishing, you will see that they do not dip their beaks straight down, as do other fish-catching birds; the pelicans put their heads sideways, and then dip their long pouched bills, as if they were going to draw a net. Into these pouches go the fish they catch, and thence down into their nets, which they still carry inside them, though they never bring them out now as in the days of Goolayyahlee, the great fishing wirreenun, who gave all his tribe the deep pouches which hang on to their long yellow bills, to use instead of the net which each carries inside him, though these are very miniature editions of the original Goolayyahlee's net, but yet big enough to let the tribe still bear his name, which means one having a net.

At right: "After stray cattle." Below left: "Driving cattle." Illustrations by Edward Whymper for Howard Willoughby in *Australian Pictures Drawn from Pen and Pencil* (London: The Religious Tract Society, 1886).

Week Twenty-Four:
THE MARANOA DROVERS

The night is dark and stormy, and the sky is clouded o'er;
   Our horses we will mount and ride away,
To watch the squatters' cattle through the darkness of the night,
   And we'll keep them on the camp till break of day.

CHORUS
For we're going, going, going to Gunnedah so far,
      And we'll soon be into sunny New South Wales;
We shall bid farewell to Queensland, with its swampy
      coolibah—
      Happy drovers from the sandy Maranoa.

When the fires are burning bright through the darkness of the night,
   And the cattle camping quiet, well, I'm sure
That I wish for two o'clock when I call the other watch—
   This is droving from the sandy Maranoa.

Our beds made on the ground, we are sleeping all so sound
   When we're wakened by the distant thunder's roar,
And the lightning's vivid flash, followed by an awful crash—
   It's rough on drovers from the sandy Maranoa.

We are up at break of day, and we're all soon on the way,
    For we always have to go ten miles or more;
It don't do to loaf about, or the squatter will come out—
    He's strict on drovers from the sandy Maranoa.

We shall soon be on the Moonie, and we'll cross the Barwon, too;
    Then we'll be out upon the rolling plains once more;
We'll shout "Hurrah! for old Queensland, with its swampy coolibah,
    And the cattle that come off the Maranoa."
        ANDREW BARTON "BANJO" PATERSON
                (1864–1941)

WORKS CITED

Alcott, Louisa May. *Our Young Folks*, Vol. I, No. IV. April 1865. "Nelly's Hospital." Trowbridge, J. T. and Hamilton, Gail, and Larcom, Lucy (eds.) Boston: Ticknor and Fields, pp. 267–277.

Arnason, Jón. *Icelandic Legends*. Translated by Eiríkur Magnússon and George E. J. Powell. "The Money-Chest." London: Richard Bentley, 1864, pp. 222–226.

Beckwith, Martha Warren. *Jamaica Anansi Stories*. "The Grave." New York: American Folk-Lore Society, 1924, pp. 25–26.

Brooks, Eva Cannon. *Francisco, Our Little Argentine Cousin*. "Francisco's Home." Boston: L. C. Page & Company, 1910, pp. 1–14.

Burk, Martha Cannary. *Life and Adventures of Calamity Jane by Herself*. Billings, MT, c. 1896.

Burt, Mary E., ed. *Poems Every Child Should Know*. "O Captain! My Captain!" by Walt Whitman. New York: Doubleday, Page & Co., 1904, p. 57.

Clark, Charles Badger. *Grass-Grown Trails*. "The Buffalo Trail." Boston: Richard G. Badger, 1917, p. 62.

Clark, Kate McCosh. *Maori Tales and Legends*: "Tereté, The Boy in the Moon." London: David Nutt, 1896, pp. 84–89.

Cox, John Harrington. *Folk-Songs of the South*. "Ballad of John Henry." Cambridge, MA: Harvard University Press, 1925, pp. 185–186.

Crockett, Davy. "Crockett's Fight with a Catfish." *Davy Crockett's Almanack, of Wild Sports in the West, and Life in the Backwoods*. Vol. 1, No. 2. Nashville, TN: Snag & Sawyer, 1836.

———. "Heroine of Kaintuck," *The Crockett Almanac*. Vol. 2, No. 2. Nashville, TN: Snag & Sawyer, 1840.

———. "Mrs. Cuttle and the Catamount," *The Crockett Almanac*. Vol. 2, No. 3. Nashville, TN: Ben Harding, 1841.

"Crooked Mick." *The Sun*. Kalgoorlie, Western Australia, 3 May, 1903.

De la Selva, Salomón. *Tropical Town and Other Poems*. "My Nicaragua." New York: John Lane and Company, 1918, pp. 12–13.

Dickinson, Asa Don. *The Children's Book of Thanksgiving Stories*. "The First Thanksgiving" by Albert F. Blaisdell and Francis K. Ball. New York: Doubleday, Page, and Company, 1915, pp. 67–71.

Dickinson, Emily. *Poems: Second Series*. "In the Garden." Todd, Mabel Loomis, and T. W. Higginson, eds. Boston: Roberts Brothers Publishers, 1891, pp. 140–141.

Dorson, Richard M. *Davy Crockett, American Comic Legend*. "Katy Goodgrit and the Wolves." New York: Spiral Press for Rockland Editions, 1939, pp. 52–53.

Eastman, Charles A., and Elaine Goodale Eastman. *Wigwam Evenings: Sioux Folk Tales Retold*. "The Frogs and the Crane." Boston: Little, Brown, and Company, 1928, pp. 19–24.

Eells, Elsie Spicer. *Fairy Tales From Brazil: How and Why Tales from Brazilian Folk-Lore*. "How the Toad Got His Bruises" and "Why the Tiger and the Stag Fear Each Other." New York: Dodd, Mead & Company, 1917, pp. 23–39 and pp. 61–69.

Goodrich, Samuel [Peter Parley, pseud.]. *The Boys' and Girls' Library; Containing a Variety of Useful and Instructive Reading, Selected from Eminent Writers for Youth*. "The Baby House." London: H. G. Collins, 1851, pp. 174–182.

Gould, Hannah Flagg. *Poems*. Vol. I. "The Frost." Boston: Hilliard, Gray, & Co., 1839, pp. 32–33.

Hale, Lucretia P. *The Peterkin Papers*. "The Peterkins Try to Become Wise." Boston: Houghton Mifflin Company, 1914, pp. 24–28.

Jackson, Helen Hunt. "Colorado Snow-Birds." *St. Nicholas: Scribner's Illustrated Magazine for Girls and Boys.* New York: Scribner and Co. Vol. II, Nov. 1874 to Nov. 1875, pp. 330–331.

———. *Poems.* "September." Boston: Roberts Brothers, 1892, pp. 189–190.

Judson, Katharine Berry. *Myths and Legends of Alaska.* "The Naming of the Birds." Chicago: A.C. McClurg & Co., 1911, pp. 66–69.

Larned, W. T. *American Indian Fairy Tales.* "The Child of the Evening Star," "The Little Boy and Girl in the Clouds," and "The Fairy Bride." Joliet, IL: P. F. Volland Co., 1921, no page numbers.

Laughead, W. B. *The Marvelous Exploits of Paul Bunyan.* "Paul Bunyan's Family and Inventions," "Paul Bunyan's Animals and Insects," and "Feeding Paul Bunyan's Crew." Minneapolis, MN: The Red River Lumber Company, 1922.

Longfellow, Henry Wadsworth. *The Belfry of Bruges and Other Poems.* "The Arrow and the Song." Cambridge, MA: John Owen, 1846, 102–103.

Lowell, Amy. *A Dome of Many-Coloured Glass.* "The Pleiades" and "Sea Shell." Boston: Houghton Mifflin Company, 1912, pp. 138–139 and 125.

Macmillan, Cyrus. *Canadian Fairy Tales.* "Great Heart and the Three Tests," "How Rabbit Deceived Fox," and "How Raven Brought Fire to the Indians." Toronto: S. B. Gundy, 1922, pp. 58–66, 96–103, and 73–81.

Mathews, Cornelius. *The Indian Fairy Book from the Original Legends.* "The Boy Who Set a Snare for the Sun." New York: Allen Brothers, 1869, pp. 17–22.

McLaughlin, Marie L. *Myths and Legends of the Sioux.* "White Plume." Bismarck, ND: Bismarck Tribune Company, 1916, pp. 156–169.

Miller, Olive Beaupré. *Through Fairy Halls of My Bookhouse.* "The Fisherman Who Caught the Sun." Chicago: The Bookhouse for Children, 1920, pp. 206–208.

Montgomery, Lucy Maud. "Charlotte's Quest." *The Family Herald*, 1933.

———. "Christmas at Red Butte." *East and West*, Dec. 25, 1909.

Moore, Clement C. *A Visit from Saint Nicholas*. New York: James G. Gregory, 1862.

O'Reilly, Edward. "The Saga of Pecos Bill." *The Century Illustrated Monthly Magazine v. 106*. 1923 May–Oct.

Parker, K. Langloh. *More Australian Legendary Tales*. "Goolayyahlee the Pelican." London: D. Nutt, 1989, p. 57–60.

Paterson, A. B. *The Old Bush Songs*. "The Maranoa Drovers." Sydney: Angus and Robertson, 1905, pp. 99–100.

Patten, William, Ed. *The Junior Classics, A Library for Boys and Girls. Volume 7*. "Old Johnny Appleseed" by Elizabeth Harrison. New York: P. F. Collier & Sons, 1912, pp. 480–485.

Payne, John Howard. *Clari; or the Maid of Milan: an Opera*. "Home, Sweet Home." London: John Miller, 1823.

Pierson, Clara Dillingham. *Among the Meadow People*. "The Young Robin Who Was Afraid to Fly." New York: E. P. Dutton & Company, 1899, pp. 61–70.

Pratt, Charles Trowbridge. *Wide Awake*. "A Case of Coincidence" by Rose Terry Cooke. Boston: D. Lothrop & Company, 1883, pp. 15–19.

Pyle, Katharine. *Wonder Tales from Many Lands*. "Mudjee Monedo" and "The King of the Buffaloes." London: George G. Harrap & Company Ltd. 1920, pp. 114–125 and 81–87.

Richards, Laura E. *The Green Satin Gown*. "Little Benjamin." Boston: Dana Estes and Company, 1903, pp. 81–111.

———. *Tirra Lirra: Rhymes Old and New*. "Eletelephony." Boston: Little, Brown and Company, 1902, p. 31.

Sandburg, Carl. *Chicago Poems*. "Fog." New York: Henry Holt and Company, 1916, p. 71.

———. *Rootabaga Stories*. "How the Animals Lost Their Tails and Got Them Back Traveling from Philadelphia to Medicine Hat." New York: Harcourt, Brace and Company, 1922, pp. 213–230.

Seibert, T. Lawrence. *Casey Jones the Brave Engineer.* (sheet music) Los Angeles, CA: Southern California Music Company, 1909.

Sulte, Benjamin. *Histoire de Montferrand, L'athlete Canadien.* "Joe Mufferaw." Montreal : Camire et Braseau, 1884.

Teasdale, Sara. *Helen of Troy and Other Poems.* "The Kind Moon." New York: G. P. Putnam's Sons, The Knickerbocker Press, 1911, pp. 105–106.

———. *Rivers to the Sea.* "The Cloud." New York: The MacMillan Company, 1917, p. 62.

Thaxter, Celia. *The Poems of Celia Thaxter.* "The Sandpiper." Boston, MA: Houghton and Mifflin, 1871, pp. 18–19.

Trowbridge, John Townsend. *The Vagabonds, and Other Poems.* "An Evening at the Farm." Boston: Fields, Osgood, and Co., 1869, pp. 132–134.

Twain, Mark. *Adventures of Tom Sawyer.* "The Glorious Whitewasher" (Chapter 2). Hartford, CT: The American Publishing Co., 1884, pp. 26–30.

Wait, Frona Eunice. *The Stories of El Dorado.* "The Plumed Serpent, Quetzalcoatl." San Francisco: Sunset Press, 1904, pp. 109–116.

Walker, Annie Louisa. (Also known as Mary Ann Walker) *Leaves from the Backwoods.* "The Night Cometh." Montreal: John Lovell, 1861, pp. 42–43.

Washburne, Marion Foster. *Indian Legends.* "How the Bear Family Got Its Name." Chicago: Rand McNally & Company, 1915, pp. 117–123.

Westbury, Atha. *Australian Fairy Tales.* "King Dunce." London: Ward, Lock, & Co., Limited, 1897, pp. 91–97.

Whittier, John Greenleaf. "Barbara Frietchie." *Atlantic Monthly.* Vol XII. Boston: Ticknor and Fields: October, 1863.

———. *The Poetical Works of John Greenleaf Whittier, Volume II.* "The Pumpkin." Boston: Houghton, Mifflin and Company, 1892, pp. 107–109.